PERELMAN'S

Home Companion

A COLLECTOR'S ITEM
(THE COLLECTOR BEING S. J. PERELMAN)
OF 36 OTHERWISE UNAVAILABLE PIECES
BY HIMSELF

1955

SIMON AND SCHUSTER · New York

PUBLISHED BY SIMON AND SCHUSTER, INC.
ROCKEFELLER CENTER, 630 FIFTH AVENUE
NEW YORK 20, N. Y.

"*Whose* Lady Nicotine?" "Dental or Mental, I Say It's Spinach," "If an In-Law Meet an Outlaw," "Why Boys Leave Home," "Let Sleeping Dogs Lie," "Your Move, General Sarnoff," and "Which Way to the Stylish Stouts?" appeared originally in *The Saturday Evening Post*. Copyright 1943 and 1944 by The Curtis Publishing Company.

"En Garde, Messieurs! Change Your Oil?" appeared originally in *Broun's Nutmeg.*

"Ms. Found in a Bottle of Firewater" appeared originally in *Funny Bone.*

"Quiet, Please" appeared originally in *The Dream Department.*

The remaining twenty-six pieces appeared originally in *The New Yorker.*

Most of the pieces in this collection are reprinted from *Look Who's Talking*, Random House, 1940, *The Dream Department*, Random House, 1943, and *Keep It Crisp*, Random House, 1946.

FIRST PRINTING

LIBRARY OF CONGRESS CATALOG CARD NUMBER: 55–10046
MANUFACTURED IN THE UNITED STATES OF AMERICA
BY KINGSPORT PRESS, INC., KINGSPORT, TENN.

For Adam

CONTENTS

Contents

FOREWORD

Like every bore who, seeking to anesthetize his audience into a state of docility, prefaces his speech with the coy disclosure that he is reminded of a story about two Irishmen, I am reminded of one that seems to have a certain relevance to the present proceedings. It appears that one of Augustus Caesar's legionary captains returned to Rome from a tour of duty in the Western Empire dragging two rather unusual captives at his chariot wheel. They were Irish gladiators, undersized but muscular little chaps with crinkly red hair, clad in green jerkins secured by massive leather belts, and their prowess was common gossip around every campfire in Gaul. The proprietor of a small neighborhood amphitheater off the Appian Way, who chanced to be casting about for a Saturday-night attraction, heard about the pair and conceived the idea of matching them against a cageful of Scythian tigers and a few unreconstructed Sarmatians left over from a campaign in Hither Asia.

From the beginning, the outcome of the match was never in doubt for an instant; the Irishmen spat on their hands, waded in, and within three minutes the air was full of dismembered Scythian tigers and former Sarmatians. Naturally, word of their stamina spread quickly through the taverns, the baths, and the lupanars frequented by the sporting fancy, and the manager of a somewhat larger stadium booked them for another engagement, this time against a pride of Numidian lions and some exceptionally fractious Libyan elephants. The carnage this time was even more devastating. Fragments of lion and splintered ivory rained down on the spectators; the arena, in the words of a contemporary sports writer, was a veritable shambles, and when the referee finally stopped the fight, only one lion was still alive, cowering behind a barricade and mewing for mercy.

Just as all Rome was buzzing about the paladins, there arrived from the steppes of Cappadocia a fainting, half-exhausted courier who bore truly wondrous news. Seven weeks earlier, he related, an obscure tribe of nomads had accidentally discovered a live mastodon imprisoned in a glacier. Under the supervision of the governor of the province, gigantic bonfires had been set, the surrounding ice thawed, and the beast captured after a Homeric struggle. It had then been trussed up aboard an enormous sledge four hundred cubits long, and even now was being arduously hauled toward the Eternal City by two thousand Thessalonian hostages lashed by brutal overseers. Popular excitement, to use Suetonius' inimitable phrase, ran at fever pitch. Almost the first Roman to grasp the possibilities was a small, dynamic showman universally regarded as the foremost impresario of his day, a Latin version of Billy Rose. Why not pit the mastodon, he suggested in a burst of inspired megalomania, against the fighting Irish at a gala performance in the Colosseum for the Vestal Virgins Fund? The words were hardly out of his mouth before long queues began forming at the box office. By nightfall of the same day, every seat had been sold out, and competition for tickets had become so keen that a well-known senator was rumored to have paid thirteen thousand sesterces for one and thrown in his wife as lagniappe. There was, in short, a marked air of anticipation.

On the afternoon of the epochal contest, under a hot and cloudless sky, the interior of the Colosseum presented an unforgettable sight. Tremendous awnings of saffron-yellow silk had been spread over the galleries to shield the spectators from the sun; musicians, clowns, and tumblers wandered through the crush, vying with each other to divert the audience; and to further swell the hullabaloo, sweetmeat sellers, necromancers, and bagmen hawking every sort of merchandise from aphrodisiacs to trained crickets cried aloud their wares. Down in the parterre boxes were visible the patricians, the administrative elite in their purple togas, and the creme of café society—elderly demireps attended by their cicisbeos, languid young exquisites redolent of perfume, reigning courtesans a-glitter with jewels. None of them, of course, paid the slightest attention to the preliminary events designed to whet the appetite of the plebes, the bear-baiting and the consumption by famished wolves of a cell of Christian agitators. Everyone awaited the electrifying moment when the mastodon, released from his subterranean dungeon and properly maddened by spear thrusts, would engage his tiny adversaries in combat. The two people in the amphitheater least concerned, however, were the Irishmen themselves. As they lounged before the gladitorial dugout, waiting for the parti-colored sand of the arena to be refurbished and negligently acknowledging the plaudits of the mob, they flexed their thews and discussed their meteoric rise to success.

"You know, life's pretty amazing," one observed. "Fifteen months ago, we were just a couple of malodorous gossoons in a Fenian bog with our fundaments painted blue, grateful for the infrequent and moldy tater that came our way. Today, alanna, we're the toast of the town, the idols of the populace, the envy of the civilized world. Faix, if you read it in a book, you'd hardly credit it."

"You're telling me?" his colleague responded. "Listen to something that happened to me only last night. I'm laying around my room, reading a trashy Greek novel, when in comes the head chamberlain of the court, begging me to have dinner with the Empress Livia in her private apartments. Well, I slip into a fresh tunic, repair to those private apartments, and what do I find? Scenes of luxury and sybaritism unimaginable to us mere earthlings. The place is heavy with the scent of frankincense and myrrh, all the rarest essences of Araby and Ind. Ranged along one wall is a trestle table which it's groaning with the most succulent viands—dormice baked in honey, swans' knees, peacock tongues flavored with horse-radish, storks in ginger, suckling pigs that when you carve them live thrushes fly out. But the most toothsome morsel by far and away is the Empress herself.

She's reclining like a great tawny cat on a dais of Tyrian purple; her hair is powdered with gold dust, her eyes be-rimmed with kohl, and she's garbed in a sheath of gold lamé they must have poured her into, pinned together at the corsage by a single flawless emerald the size of a County Clare potato. Well, we dined famously, just the two of us, exchanging gay bavardage and washing down the feast with many an amphora of crusty Falernian, and at length, having satisfied the inner man, I'm sprawled out at the Empress's feet idly nibbling on a pomegranate. All of a sudden, this inexplicable whim seizes Livia. 'Look, big boy,' she says in a husky whisper, 'are you really as strong as they claim? I'd like to feel your muscle.' Well, what could I do? After all, it's an imperial whim and you can't gainsay a Caesar else she'll crack your noggin like an egg. So I peel back the sleeve of my tunic, flex my biceps, and extend my arm. Now comes the singular part. As she's straining over to touch it, this emerald on her bodice bursts its moorings, the sheath flies open. . . . Did you ever see the statue of Venus Callipyge over there on the Via Flaminia?"

"Yes, yes, a million times," the other panted. "But go on—don't stop! What happened?"

"What happened?" repeated his friend, the reminiscent smile abruptly fading from his face. "I'll tell you some other time. Here comes that -------- mastodon."

The mastodon with which the reader now finds himself confronted may, admittedly, turn out to be a mouse, but I chose the term advisedly. Most of the pieces hereinafter contained have been entombed a good while in books of mine that are no longer available, and it is also conceivable that the time devoted to reading them may interrupt something infinitely more provocative. Nevertheless, if they arouse no other emotion, they may produce the same sense of delicious revulsion one experiences in a hall of dinosaurs or a medical museum. . . . As for those portentous disquisitions I am often besought to make on the nature of humor, its place in our changing world, and my opinion of it as a livelihood, I'll tell you some other time. Here comes that - - - - - - - groceryman.

S. J. PERELMAN

No Dearth of Mirth— Fill Out the Coupon!

If, about Christmas time, you notice me sporting a curious insignia on my vest, a stipple of small white spots as though I had been eating Royal Riviera pears with a spoon, it may interest you to know that you are looking at a full-fledged, bonafide member of the original Fruit-of-the-Month Club. This is not to be confused with the Fruit-of-the-Loom Club, an organization I also belong to, which allows me to sleep an hour later than nonmembers, or the Fruit-of-the-Moola Club, a society that sells me United States currency at ten per cent off the list price. No, the Fruit-of-the-Month Club is a powerful and exclusive sodality originating at the Bear Creek Orchards in Medford, Oregon, consecrated to supplying me and mine with Royal Riviera pears in December, grapefruit in January, apples in February, rare preserves in April, plums in June, summer pears in August, peaches in September, and Lavelle grapes in October. I became a member of this singular brotherhood quite by chance; a trifling favor I did a stranger earned his gratitude.

Late one afternoon several months ago I was seated at a rear table in Sardi's, browsing through *Billboard* over a cup of bohea, when a conversation near by arrested my attention. Two plausible characters in billycock hats, whose fly manner and diamond-paste stickpins stamped them theatrical promoters, were inveigling a defenseless old cotton converter into backing a costume drama.

"Why, it's as safe as houses," purred one of them. "Tell him the prologue again, Skins."

"Sure," agreed the individual addressed by that unsavory appellation. "We open in an Italian grotto back in the sixteenth century. That's on account of the public's crazy about the sixteenth century."

"Is that so?" inquired the converter. "I didn't know that."

"Just can't get enough of it," Skins assured him. "That's all they ask for in the ticket agencies—a good meaty show about the sixteenth century. Well, anyhow, our leading man is discovered in this grotto, writing on a parchment scroll with a feather. Pretty soon he sprinkles sand over the manuscript, pulls a bell rope, and his apprentice comes in. 'There, Giovanni, it's finished,' he says. 'Rush it to the printer.' 'What are you going to call it, Signor Boccaccio?' says the apprentice. '*The Decameron*,' says Boccaccio. 'It may be just a lot of smutty stories to you, but some day this here vellum will be immortal.' "

"Yes, that's very effective," said the converter thoughtfully. "And you say Charles Laughton's offered to play Boccaccio?"

"We've got him under wraps at the Hotel Edison," the first promoter replied smoothly. "He starts rehearsing the minute your check is dry. Here," he said, unscrewing a fountain pen. "Just make it out to Thimblerig Productions." My ire boiled over at their pettifoggery and, rising, I laid about me with the folded *Billboard* to such effect that the blackguards took to their heels, howling with pain. The victim, once I had exposed their duplicity, was naturally all gratefulness—filled my case with cigars, offered to convert some cotton for me, besought me to share a home-cooked meal he had in his pocket. He finally gave me my liberty in exchange for my address, and a few days later a handsomely engraved certificate informed me that I had been proposed for and elected to the Fruit-of-the-Month Club.

It recently occurred to me while munching the alternate November selection, a rather mealy Winesap, that though there are countless kindred services designed to provide people with books, flowers, records, regional delicacies, and even diapers, no machinery has ever been devised to furnish them old jokes on a seasonal basis. "Would not the discerning," I asked myself, "welcome an association patterned after the Fruit-of-the-Month Club, purveying flavorful, old-fashioned gags—the kind of time-honored nifties Father used to make?" In my mind's eye, I envisioned thousands of subscribers to the Jape-of-the-Month Club receiving at specified intervals their hand-culled jokes packed in dry ice, suitable for use in domestic arguments, encounters with bill collectors, visits to the dentist—in short, in all the trivial, everyday contingencies that recur throughout the year. Simultaneously, it struck me that the only person in America capable of grasping the magnitude of the scheme was Barnaby Chirp. Brilliant young publisher, writer, book reviewer, anthologist, columnist, and flaneur, Chirp had fathered many a compendium of hilarious rib-ticklers. His latest, *Laughing Gasp,* had sold six hundred and fifty thousand copies prior to publication; so well had it sold, in fact, that a first edition was never published. His motto, "Git thar fustest with the mustiest jokes," indubitably made him my man, and I rushed to his office to broach the idea. He jumped at it.

"It's the cat's pajamas—a peachamaroot!" he proclaimed, jumping at it. "Here, let me get this stuff out of the way so we can talk." Turning back to his desk, he delivered two radio broadcasts into a lapel microphone, organized a ten-cent-book cartel, wrote a thirty-five-thousand-word preface to *Higgledy-Piggledy: An Omnibus of Jocose Jugoslav*

Stories, and sold the Scandinavian dramatic rights of *Laughing Gasp* to a small Danish producer in the bottom drawer. "Now then," he said, swinging toward me, "we'll fix the annual membership fee of the Jape-of-the-Month Club at twenty-five hundred a year."

"Isn't that a bit steep?" I asked.

"Not for people of discrimination, those who can afford the finer things," said Chirp. "We've got to winnow out the ragtag and bobtail. The next step is to find an impartial board of judges to choose our monthly wheezes. How about a publisher, a writer, a book reviewer, an anthologist, and a columnist?"

"Good notion," I said. "What say to a panel like this: Nelson Doubleday, MacKinlay Kantor, Harry Hansen, Whit Burnett, and Louis Sobol?"

"Too diverse," he said. "They'd never get on. I'll tell you what—why don't we get one man who's *all* those things? Then there wouldn't be any silly squabbling."

"Listen," I said, "anyone who's all those things is a genius."

"Why, thank you," said Chirp, coloring with pleasure. "I like you, too. Of course, I don't know whether I can crowd the job into my schedule, but I'll do my best. Now, exactly how would the Jape-of-the-Month function?"

"Well," I said, "during January and February we'd ship our subscribers good, pre-tested chestnuts about the weather. For example, if someone complains to you of the cold, you advise him to go to Mexico. He naturally asks why. 'Because,' you tell him, 'down there it's chili today and hot tamale.' "

"Fan my brow," giggled Chirp, scribbling a note on a pad. "That's a sockdolager! Mind if I use it in my column?"

"Not at all," I said. "That's where I read it last week. In July and August, applying the same principle, we mail our members warm-weather rejoinders. Suppose you're asked whether it's hot enough for you. 'Hot?' you say. 'It's so hot I feed my chickens cracked ice to keep 'em from laying hard-boiled eggs!' "

"I've heard that one somewhere before," muttered Chirp dubiously. "Ah, what the hell, I can always credit it to Dorothy Parker. What sort of jokes could we guarantee the rest of the year?"

"Whatever the occasion demands," I answered. "In April, when your wife's mother generally pays a visit, we send out our Easter special. 'They ought to call our car a mother-in-law model,' you tell your wife. 'Why is that?' she asks. 'Because it's got a crank in the back seat.' Along about June, after your son's home from college, you'd say to your friends, 'Yes, Willie's got his B.A. and his M.A., but his P.A. still supports him.' See how it works?"

"Aha," said Chirp, "and I'll tell you what's wrong with it. It's too sophisticated for the average person. You've got to hoke it up."

"How do you mean?"

"Well, take that January selection. I'd change it to 'Down in Mexico it's chilly today and hot tomorrow.' "

"But what becomes of the point?" I asked.

"The point, the point!" bawled Chirp. "Everybody's always griping about the point! How do you think I'd fill my column every week if all the stories had to have a point?"

"You win," I yielded. "After all, you've got your finger on the popular pulse."

"Right," he said. "I find that if you leave the nub out of your anecdotes once in a while, it intrigues the reader enormously. Here, look at the response I got on last week's column." He opened a drawer, took out a response, and showed it to me. Then he leaned back and gave me the dazzling smile with which he ushers in any discussion involving money. "O.K., son, how do we set this thing up?"

"Well," I said haltingly, "I suppose that since I thought of it—"

"Precisely," he finished. "You're certainly entitled to a share of the profits." He drew a pie chart on his pad, snipped out a minute wedge with a pair of scissors, and handed it to me. "There's your cut," he explained. "The rest goes into advertising, research, judges' fees, stuff like that. Can you wrap bundles?"

"Gee," I protested, "I saw myself in more of an executive role."

"Oh, a white-collar snob, eh?" sneered Chirp. "What are

you afraid of—soiling your hands? I expect you to get out and do some canvassing, too. Ever been a salesman?"

"No," I said, stealthily reaching for my hat, "but I heard a pip of a quip about one yesterday."

"You did?" Chirp caught up his pencil, his eyes gleaming.

"Yes," I said. "It seems that a salesman called Moss Hart stopped at a Bucks County farmhouse one night. The farmer's daughter, who was named Dorothy Parker, asked what his profession was. 'I'm a travelling man,' he said. 'Yes,' she riposted, 'I can see that by the bags under your eyes.' " As Chirp rocked back in his chair, helpless with laughter, I silently stole out the door. I left behind a pair of arctics, a solid gold briefcase, and a little portion of my reason, but I don't really care. Who would, with that kind of money coming in like clockwork every month?

How Sharper Than a Serpent's Tooth

THE OTHER EVENING, with nobody levelling a gun at my temple, I deserted a well-sprung armchair and a gripping novel, sloshed forty blocks uptown in a freezing rain, and, together with five hundred other bats, hung from the rafters at Loew's Strabismus to see Joan Crawford's latest vehicle, *Mildred Pierce*. Certain critics, assessing the film, maintained that Miss Crawford rose to heights never before scaled. Whether she did or not, I certainly did; the only person higher than me was the projectionist, who kept flicking ashes down my coat collar and sneezing so convulsively that twice during the performance my head rolled down the balcony steps.

Oh, I was kept busy, I can tell you, running downstairs to retrieve it and following the story at the same time. Yet even under these trying conditions, aggravated by the circumstance that someone had liberated a powerful sleep-inducing drug among the audience, I was gripped by a brief passage between the star and her daughter, played by Ann Blyth. It had been established that Joan, eager to give the child every advantage, had worked tirelessly as a waitress, shielding the fact from her, and had eventually built up a chain of restaurants. Ann, though, inevitably discovers her mother's plebeian calling, and at the proper kinetic moment her disdain boils over in a speech approximately as follows: "Faugh, you disgust me. You reek of the kitchen, of blue plates and sizzling platters. You bring with you the smell of grease and short-order frying, you—you restaurateuse, you!" At that juncture, unluckily, the projectionist sneezed again, with such force that I was blown clear into the lobby and out into Times Square, and deciding that it would be tempting fate to return to my perch, I sloshed quickly downtown while the sloshing was good.

Reviewing the scene in my mind (or, more properly, what remained of the scene in what remained of my mind), I realized that however fruity the phrasing, its psychology was eminently sound. The instinct to conceal one's true livelihood from the kiddies, for fear of their possible scorn, is as normal as snoring. A highly solvent gentleman in Forest Hills, a vestryman and the father of three, once told me in wine that for thirty years, under twelve different pseudonyms, he had supplied the gamiest kind of pulp fiction to *Snappy Stories* and *Flynn's*, although his children believed him to be a stockbroker. The plumper the poke, the more painful is any reference to its origin.

The most recent victim of indiscreet babble of this sort is Barbara Hutton Mdivani Reventlow Grant, with whose predicament Charles Ventura lately concerned himself in his society column in the *World-Telegram*. Wrote Mr. Ventura: "Relations between the chain-store heiress and her ex-husband, Kurt, are still strained. Barbara tells friends her most recent annoyance from Kurt came with the discovery he had gone out of his way to tell Lance his mother's money came from the ten-cent store."

The item poses all sorts of interesting questions. What constitutes going out of your way to tell a lad his mother's money came from forty or fifty thousand ten-cent stores? How did Lance take the news? Did he, in the first shock of revelation, force his father to his knees and demand a retraction of the slur? Did he fling himself with a choked cry into the Countess's lap, all tears and disillusion, or did he heap coals on her head? Mr. Ventura does not say. Mr. Ventura, it would seem, is an old tease. With the implication that he has other fish to fry, he leaps straightway into the domestic problems of slim, attractive Yvette Helene LeRoux Townsend, leaving me in my ragged shawl out in the snow, nursing Barbara Hutton's predicament. I hope that the dimly analogous situation which follows, served up for convenience in a dramatic fricassee, may shed some light on the matter and bring chaos out of confusion.

[*Scene: The library of the luxurious Park Avenue triplex of Mr. and Mrs. Milo Leotard Allardyce DuPlessis Weatherwax. The furnishings display taste but little ostentation: a couple of dozen Breughels, fifteen or twenty El Grecos, a sprinkling of Goyas, a smidgen of Vermeers. The room has a lived-in air: a fistful of loose emeralds lies undusted in an ashtray, and the few first folios in evidence are palpably dog-eared. The curtain rises on a note of marital discord. Octavia Weatherwax, a chic, poised woman in her mid-forties, has just picked up a bust of Amy Lowell by Epstein and smashed it over her husband's head. Milo, a portly, well-groomed man of fifty, spits out a tooth, catches up a bust of Epstein by Amy Lowell, and returns the compliment.*]

OCTAVIA (*brushing plaster from her coiffure*): Listen, Milo, we can't go on this way.

MILO: Why not? I've still got this left. (*He picks up a bust of Amy Epstein by Lowell Thomas.*)

OCTAVIA: No, no, this is the handwriting on the wall. Our marriage is washed up—napoo—*ausgespielt*.

MILO: Maybe you're right. I've felt for some time that things haven't been the same between us.

OCTAVIA: Oh, well, the fat's in the fire. How are we to break the news to Rapier?

MILO: Rapier? What Rapier is that?

OCTAVIA: Why, our nineteen-year-old son, which he's home from Yale on his midyears and don't suspicion that his folks are rifting.

MILO: Oh, yes. Where is our cub at the present writing?

OCTAVIA: In the tack room, furbishing up the accoutrements of his polo ponies.

MILO (*acidly*): Far better off to be furbishing up on his Euclid, lest he drag the name of Weatherwax through the scholastic mire.

OCTAVIA: Shhhh, here he comes now. (*The sound of expensive Scotch brogues approaching on a parquet floor is heard, an effect achieved by striking two coconut shells together.*) If you need me, I shall be laying down on my lounge with a vinegar compress. (*She exits as Rapier enters —a rather awkward bit of stagecraft, as they trip over each other, but if the play runs, the property man can always saw another door in the set. Rapier, albeit somewhat spoiled, is a blueblood to his fingertips, carries his head and feet as though to the manner born.*)

RAPIER: Hiya, Jackson. What's buzzin', cousin?

MILO: Humph. Is that some more of your new-fangled college slang?

RAPIER: Don't be a sherbet, Herbert. (*Lighting a gold-monogrammed Egyptian Prettiest*) What's cookin', good-lookin'?

MILO (*gravely*): Son, I'm not going to mince words with you.

RAPIER: Don't mince, quince. I'm waitin', Satan.

Milo: My boy, the Weatherwax union has blown a gasket. Our frail matrimonial bark, buffeted by the winds of temperament, has foundered on the shoals of incompatibility.

Rapier: Get in the groove, fatso. I don't latch onto that long-hair schmaltz.

Milo: To employ the vulgate, your mother and I have phhht.

Rapier (*with quick sympathy*): That's rum, chum.

Milo: Yes, it's hard on us oldsters, but it isn't going to be easy for you, either.

Rapier (*frightened*): You mean I've got to go to work?

Milo: Certainly not. As long as there's a penny of your mother's money left, we'll make out somehow.

Rapier: Look, guv'nor, I . . . that is, me . . . aw, cripes, can I ask you something man to man?

Milo (*aside*): I was afraid of this.

Rapier: Well, I've been running with a pretty serious crowd up at New Haven—lots of bull sessions about swing and stuff—and I've been wondering. Where does our money come from?

Milo (*evasively*): Why—er—uh—the doctor brings it. In a little black bag.

Rapier: Aw, gee, Dad, I'm old enough to know. *Please.*

Milo: There, there. Now run along and play with your ponies.

Rapier: Wouldn't you rather tell me than have me learn it in the gutter?

MILO: We-e-ell, all right, but my, you children grow up quick nowadays. Have you ever heard of the Weatherwax All-Weather Garbage Disposal Plan?

RAPIER: You—you mean whereby garbage is disposed of in all weathers by having neatly uniformed attendants call for and remove it?

MILO: Yes. That is the genesis of our scratch.

RAPIER (*burying his face in his hands*): Oh, Daddy, I want to die!

MILO: Steady on, lad. After all, think of the millions which their flats would be a welter of chicken bones, fruit peels, and old tea bags were it not for our kindly ministrations.

RAPIER (*sobbing*): I'll never be able to hold up my head in Bulldog circles again.

MILO: Nonsense. Why, you wear the keenest threads on the campus and are persona grata to myriad Eli frats.

RAPIER (*his face drawn and a new maturity in his voice*): No, Father, this is the end of halcyon days in the groves of Academe. I'm going away.

MILO: Where?

RAPIER: Somewhere beyond the horizon—to fabled Cathay or Samarkand and Ind, if need be. Anywhere I can find other values than the tinkle of money and the clang of refuse cans.

MILO (*his eyes shining*): There speaks a Weatherwax, my boy. Here, I want you to have this little keepsake.

RAPIER: What is it?

MILO: A letter of credit for seven hundred grand. It won't buy much except dreams, but it belonged to your mother.

RAPIER: Thank you, sir. (*He starts out.*)

MILO: Wait a minute, I can't let you go like this. You'll need money, introductions, shelter—

RAPIER: I'll patch up that old private railroad car of mine—the one underneath the Waldorf-Astoria.

MILO: Take ours, too. It's only using up steam.

RAPIER (*simply*): I'm sorry, Dad. From now on I walk alone. Good-by. (*He exits, colliding with his mother—there simply* must *be two doors in this set. Octavia looks back at him, puzzled.*)

OCTAVIA: Why, goodness, what ails the child? What's that exalted look on his face?

MILO: That, Octavia, is what a very great Russian named Louis Tolstoy once called "redemption."

OCTAVIA: Milo! You didn't tell—you couldn't—

MILO (*his shoulders bowed*): It just soaked in through his pores. (*Octavia, her eyes tragic, picks up a bronze caryatid, smashes it over his head, and exits. He shrugs, picks up a Greek bacchante loitering in the wings, and consoles himself.*)

CURTAIN

The Longer the Lip, the Smoother the Grift

Do young men nowadays still become hopelessly enamored of married women easily ten years their senior who have mocking, humorous mouths, eyes filled with tender raillery, and indulgent husbands? Back in the twenties, when it was a lot easier for a woman to be ten years my senior than it is now, I was privileged to know one who fitted these specifications and who inflamed me deeply. By the time the lava cooled, I found that the tender raillery in her eyes was actually pseudoblepsis, a form of myopia, and that her husband was somewhat less indulgent than I had supposed. The experience, nevertheless, had a certain salutary effect. It forever dispelled the notion I had cherished from boyhood that a mustache makes you irresistible to the opposite sex.

I grew one that summer in a dogged attempt to bridge the disparity in our ages, modelling it on those worn by the Coldstream Guards I remembered in the pages of *Chatterbox.* It was a dismal tuft—cinnamon-colored, rather spiky, inclined to droop at the corners in a depressing Mongol fashion. If I resembled anybody, which was questionable, it was Ginger Dick or Russet in W. W. Jacobs' stories. After carefully grooming and disbudding it for three weeks, I entered the lady's presence in snowy flannels, negligently plucking a round-bellied mandolin. There was no immediate reaction. At length I yawned, flicked an infinitesimal speck of zweiback from my lapel, and inquired lightly, "Notice anything different?" "God, yes," she replied in a strangled voice. "You look like a dentist. A mechanical dentist," she added cruelly, bursting into a shriek of maniacal laughter. I arose, my lip curling as far as the mustache would permit, and, stumbling over a rubber plant, swept out of her life.

I bare this early scar only to prove that my credentials are in order at a moment when mustaches, for some inexplicable reason, suddenly seem to have become especially newsworthy. As influential and responsible a journal as the New York *Post,* for instance, apparently considers them significant enough to merit a poll of opinion. A few days ago it sent its inquiring photographer out to ask five mustached citizens at random, "Is a mustache an advantage or a disadvantage to you in the business world?" Every man interviewed replied without equivocation that a mustache had aided him immeasurably in his career. All concurred that it gave them a "more mature and distinguished appearance" and inspired "confidence." One of them, a stock clerk, stated, "I am 21, and I find that the mustache makes people think I am much older, and they seem to have more confidence in me." Another, a salesman who claimed that he was known to the business world as "Lester with the Mustache," said, "A mustache seems to give the customer confidence that he is dealing with a person who knows his business."

Now, gracious knows I approve wholeheartedly of anything that tends to banish distrust and engender a universal spirit of faith, but I doubt that a few hundred hairs on the upper lip, no matter how silky, can supplant a triple-A rating in Bradstreet. The most reassuring mustaches I ever saw were those worn by automobile salesmen around Los Angeles, a notoriously factitious crew. These foxy-nosed brethren all had rich mahogany sun tans, luxuriant mustaches stiff with pomade, and prematurely white wavy hair. Max Beerbohm once observed that men with prematurely white hair are invariably charlatans. The average Hollywood foxy-nose was acutely aware of this (he was, needless to say, a constant reader of Beerbohm), and he sought to offset it by camouflaging himself with a solid, executive mustache. He fooled nobody—nobody, that is, except me.

How the particular one I recall ever tracked me to the dispiriting hacienda where I lay brooding I cannot imagine; it was the least prepossessing in a weedy suburb full of raw-food addicts, astrologers, and obscure fire worshippers. I found him smirking on the doorstep one dank forenoon as I was reaching for my morning avocado. He wore a rough shooting coat of hyper-tweed and woven wire, a primrose-yellow muffler tied Ascot fashion, brogues that had been perforated until they were simply scraps of leather, and a silver signet ring weighing just under four pounds. The twin points of his mustache were needle-sharp and he exhaled a scent of fabulously expensive cologne.

"Howdy, Aguinaldo," he saluted, clapping me familiarly on the back. "The lady of the house in?"

"I'm the lady of the house," I said coldly, sacrificing accuracy for hauteur. Before I could raise the drawbridge, he slid past me into the living room and zipped open his briefcase, his eyes taking rapid inventory of the furnishings.

"Gloomy little hole you've got here," he commented. "What do you do, store roots in it?"

"That's for me to know and you to find out," I parried. He pretended not to have heard my riposte and drew forth a limp leather manual.

"Now, here's the way it figures, Mac," he began. "The best we can do for you on a new Moosup convertible is fourteen hundred skins."

"Hey, wait a minute!" I protested. "I never—"

"Quiet!" he ordered. "I'll do the talking around here. Now, judging from this layout"—he looked about critically—"you want to buy the car on time. Suppose you let us have twelve hundred down—"

I interrupted and, mincing no words, made it clear I already owned a car that he could see on his departure, which I hoped was imminent.

"You mean that stem-winder in the driveway?" he sneered. "That's not a car—that's transportation!"

The cheap gibe at my little bluebell stung my cheeks to flame.

"It's good enough for me," I blazed, "and anyway, I'd drive a—a brewery wagon if it got me there!"

"Where?" he asked.

"Where—wherever I was going," I replied weakly.

"Where *are* you going—to a dog fight?" He chuckled. "You certainly have the clothes for it." I suddenly realized I no longer held trump cards and laid my hand authoritatively on his coat collar. He brushed it aside without rancor.

"Look, friend," he purred, "you've got me wrong. Hatcher & Gonsdorf don't sell automobiles—we sell *good will.*"

"You do?" I asked, struck by this profound merchandising philosophy.

"Of course," he said. "Do you think I'd sacrifice flesh and blood for a lousy commission? I'd rather have your friendship." His honest emotion shamed me; I saw I had done him a deep injustice.

"That hits me where I live, fellow," I said shyly. We shook hands.

"They don't come any whiter than you, old man," he said, his voice husky. "Now, get your coat. I want to see you behind the wheel of a job I've got outside. Test its fingertip control, self-annealing shock absorbers, and forty-seven big new features. I don't want you to buy it. As a matter of fact, it's not for sale."

It was either the man's hypnotic mustache or some drug like scopolamine he introduced into my coffee; anyway, on the dot of noon I issued dreamily from the Friendly Finance Company with an empty poke in one hand and the title to a new juggernaut in the other. My chest swelled with pride as I paused on the curb and surveyed its sleek black body edged with glistening chromework, its virginal white-wall tires. Then, settling my cap like Barney Oldfield's, I crawled in and pointed the nose of the machine toward the open road. Motorists and pedestrians alike bit their lips in envy as I streaked past, annihilating time and space with a casual pressure of the foot. At a traffic light I overheard two old ladies in a battered blue sedan discussing me in awed whispers. "That's Luis Escobar, the South American matinée idol," murmured one. "They say he commands upward of ninety thousand reals a picture. A woman isn't safe with a man like that." I lounged back, my eyes heavy-lidded with boredom, and contemplated trips to Baja California, the

Everglades, the Gaspé Peninsula. I might even have Buckminster Fuller design me a Dymaxion trailer, embodying certain innovations I had projected for a long time. . . .

Five miles from the Friendly Finance Company, a horrid temblor shook the motor. Some instinctive mechanical bent warned me to pull into the nearest gas station. I had barely drawn up before a mosque-shaped lubritorium when the car emitted a deep, phthisic cough. Almost simultaneously, a Marmon engine of the vintage of 1928, covered with barnacles, dropped out of the hood and lay steaming between the front wheels. Two minutes later, an incredibly handsome young man, whose prematurely white hair proclaimed him a rare mixture of charlatan and chump, crept out of the driver's seat, borrowed a nickel from the attendant, and rode home on the streetcar. He's still looking for a certain auto salesman, formerly in the employ of Hatcher & Gonsdorf—chap with a dashing black mustache. As I get the story, he wants to pull it out by the roots.

Midwinter Facial Trends

A SCENARIO WRITER I know, who had been working uninterruptedly in Hollywood for three years, finally got back to New York for a two-week vacation. He had barely unpacked his gold-backed military hairbrushes and put on a red moiré smoking jacket when a wire from his agent ordered him back to the Coast for an assignment. The young man preferred to stay, but his conscience reminded him of the two hundred and fifty thousand dollars in annuities he was carrying, and this in turn summoned up a frightening picture of a destitute old age when he might have to work on a newspaper again and ride in buses. After wrestling with himself for several hours, he decided to assert his independence. He sent back a spunky wire to the effect that he was working on a novel and could not return under any conditions unless his salary was raised to seventeen hundred and fifty dollars a week, instead of fifteen hundred. Then he forgot all about it, except to lie awake three nights and stay indoors waiting for the telephone to ring.

To nobody's surprise, the deal went through, and forty-eight hours later the scenario writer was sitting in a producer's office in Hollywood, a little worse for the plane trip and a box of sodium Amytal tablets. In a few badly chosen words the producer explained his predicament. He had a terrific story; it smelled box office a mile away. But every writer on the payroll had been stumped for the last three months by one tiny detail.

"I'll tell you the meat of the story," said the producer. "It's got plenty of spontinuity when you maul it over in your mind, only just this one little thing you got to figure out."

"Give," murmured the scenario writer, closing his eyes to indicate that his faculties were purring like a Diesel engine.

"We fade in on a street in London," began the producer, fading in on a street in London. "It's about four o'clock in the morning and I see a guy dressed in rags dragging himself along through the fog, a Lon Chaney type guy. He's all twisted and crippled up. *Voom!* All of a sudden he ducks down an areaway and knocks on a door. It opens and I see a gorgeous hallway with Chinese rugs and Ming vases. We hold the camera on it and milk whatever we can from the scene. The minute the guy's inside, he straightens up, takes off this harness, and unties his leg. What I mean is, the guy's as normal as you or me. Any audience'll buy that—am I right? Then we truck with him through a door and he's in like a hospital corridor. He pulls on rubber gloves and an operating gown—"

"Wait a minute," the writer interrupted, rising. "Am I supposed to spot laughs in this?"

"Siddown," commanded the producer. "There's a million opportunities for good crazy dialogue later on. We wipe the guy into an operating room and pan around. He's got ten, fifteen beautiful dames chained to the walls with practically nothing on, and if that don't blow the audience out of the back of the houses, I don't know show business. The legal department's taking it up with the Hays office this afternoon. We follow the guy over to a bench that's full of test tubes and scientific stuff; he pours one test tube into another and hollers, 'I got it! The life secret I been hunting for years!' Mind you, this ain't dialogue—I'm just spitballing. So then he puts a little of this life secret in a hypodermic needle and rings a gong. These two assistants wheel in a table with our leading woman on it, out like a light. Our guy rubs his hands and laughs like a hyena. He picks up the hypo, bends over our girl, and that's where you got to figure out this one thing."

"What's that?" the writer inquired suspiciously. The producer bit the end off a manufacturer's-size Corona, frustration in his eyes, and shook his head.

"What kind of a business is this guy in?" he asked helplessly.

If you are inclined to brood easily, I can guarantee that this question will tease you to the brink of hysteria. It obsessed me almost constantly until I stumbled across what may very well be the answer. It is contained in a little 134-page brochure entitled *Cosmetic Surgery*, by Charles C. Miller, M.D., published by the author in 1907. Since that day several weeks ago when I first peeped into this attractive volume, bound in red sharkskin, I have been confined to my rooms in the Albany with a fairly constant attack of the rams. As if Dr. Miller's prose style were not sufficiently graphic, the text is supplemented with half a dozen photographs and a score of drawings calculated to make your scalp tingle. I am no sissy, but I will risk a sporting flutter of half a guinea that even the brothers Mayo would have flinched under *Cosmetic Surgery*.

The author starts off casually enough with instructions for correcting outstanding ears, which range all the way from starching them to some pretty violent surgery. Personally, I have found that a short length of three-quarter-inch Manila hemp bound stoutly about the head, the knot protruding below one's felt hat, adds a rakish twist to the features and effectively prisons ears inclined to flap in the wind. A salty dash may be imparted to the ensemble by dipping the rope in tar, or even substituting oakum for hemp.

I must confess that the chapter headed "Nose with the Bulbous Tip," on page 50, fired my blood, and I read three or four pages avidly waiting for the appearance of Hercule Poirot or even Inspector Lestrade before I discovered that no crime had been committed. But on page 79, just as I finished yawning through some hints on diminishing the unduly large mouth by hemstitching it at the corners, Dr. Miller plucked the roses from my cheeks with "Marginal Tattooing as a Means of Adding to the Apparent Width of the Lips." That may not be your idea of a punchy title for the marquee of a theater, but if Boris Karloff were in it, you'd pay your six-sixty fast enough. Living as I do on the hem of the wilderness, I was not aware that "tattooing about the margin of the lips to overcome undue thinness" had become a commonplace. The technique is as follows: "The skin is punctured or pricked open with a needle. The puncturing does not extend through the skin, but merely into the true skin. [Come, come, Doctor, let's not quibble.] After the punctures have been made, the coloring is rubbed in with the point of the needle or with a slightly flattened spud. Some reaction may be expected to follow the operation, but healing is complete in a few days." Why any reaction save boredom should follow rubbing a patient's lips with a potato is not clear to me, but I suppose that if one were allergic to potatoes, one might become restless under the massage. Speaking for myself, I have always been very partial to potatoes, especially those of the cottage-fried type.

It is on page 92, with "The Formation of the Dimple," that Dr. Miller really removes the buttons from the foils. "It is my practice in these cases," he states, "to thoroughly scrub the cheek, and then, after having the patient smile, select the point where a dimple should form under ordinary circumstances. . . . I mark this point, and insert my hypodermic needle." The operative method from now on is strikingly similar to fishing for perch through a hole in the ice. The Doctor lowers a line with a bobber and a bit of red flannel, builds a fire on the patient's forehead, and sits down to warm his hands till a dimple is hooked. The patient lies there softly whimpering, "I didn't have enough trouble, I had to have dimples like Kirk Douglas yet!" And there let us leave them in the softly flickering firelight, with the thought that it will flicker much better if you pile on an occasional page out of *Cosmetic Surgery*, by Charles C. Miller.

Whose Lady Nicotine?

AT APPROXIMATELY four o'clock yesterday afternoon, the present troubadour, a one-story taxpayer in a wrinkled alpaca jacket and a repossessed Panama, was gaping into the window of Alfred Buntwell Inc., the celebrated tobacconist in Radio City. Above his balding, gargoyle head floated a feathery cloud containing a Mazda bulb labeled "Idea!" Buntwell is a name revered by pipe smokers everywhere; his briars have probably penetrated farther into the earth's far places than the Union Jack. From the steaming jungles of the Gran Chaco to the snows of Kanchanjanga, from the Hook of

Holland to the Great Barrier Reef, the white dot on the Buntwell pipe stem is the sign of the sahib. Deep in equatorial Africa, surrounded by head-hunters, Mungo Park clenched a Buntwell pipe between his teeth to maintain his fortitude; it was a battered Buntwell mouthpiece that yielded up the fate of the Franklin polar expedition.

Peering into the shop, jostled by crisp, well-fed executives hurrying toward million-dollar deals, it suddenly struck me that a Buntwell pipe was the key to my future. Here at last was a magic talisman that would transform me from a wormy, chopfallen cipher into a forceful, grim-lipped tycoon. A wave of exultation swept over me; I saw myself in the club car of the Twentieth Century Limited puffing a silver-mounted Buntwell and merging directorates with a careless nod. I too could become one of those enviable types who lounged against knotty-pine interiors in four-color advertisements, smoking their Buntwells and fiercely demanding Old Peg-leg Whisky. "Give me Old Peg-leg's satin smoothness every time," I would growl. "I like a *blended* rye."

I squared my tiny shoulders and, baring my teeth in the half-snarl befitting a major industrialist, entered the shrine. To my chagrin, no obsequious lackey sprang forward to measure my features for the correct model. A cathedral hush enveloped the shop, which had the restrained elegance of a Park Avenue jeweler's. At a chaste showcase displaying a box of panatelas marked down to a thousand dollars, a glacial salesman was attending a fierce old party with white cavalry mustaches redolent of Napoleon brandy. In the background, another was languidly demonstrating a cigarette lighter to a dowager weighed down under several pounds of diamonds. I coughed apologetically and gave the salesman a winning smile to indicate that I knew my place. The old grenadier scowled at me from under beetling brows. "Confound it, sir," he roared, "you're not at a cock fight! Blasted place is gettin' noisier than the durbar!" I cleared my throat, in which a fish bone had mysteriously lodged, and made myself as inconspicuous as possible. The salesman hastily explained that the war had brought an influx of foreigners, but his client refused to be mollified.

"Should have caned the bounder," he sputtered. "Country's goin' to the demnition bow-wows, dash it all! Now then, Harkrider, what's this infernal nonsense about my Burma cheroots?" He waved aside the salesman's excuse that a convoy had been sunk, commanded that Buntwell himself be summoned.

"But Mr. Buntwell's been dead sixty years, Major," Harkrider protested.

"None of your poppycock!" barked the major. "You tell Buntwell to bring 'em around personally by noon tomorrow or I close my account!" He stamped out, his wattles crimson with rage, and I sidled forward timidly. In a few badly chosen words, I indicated that I required a pipe.

"H'm-m-m," murmured Harkrider grudgingly, surveying

my clothes. "Just a moment." He disappeared through a curtain and engaged in a whispered consultation with the manager. I dimly overheard a phrase that sounded like "buttersnipe"; the two were obviously discussing their lunch. At length the salesman re-entered and conducted me sullenly to a showcase. After some deliberation, he extracted what appeared to be an old sycamore root fitted with a steel flange that covered the bowl.

"Know anything about pipes?" he inquired patronizingly.

"Well, not exactly," I hesitated. "I had a corncob when I was a little boy——"

"I'm not interested in reminiscences of your youth," he snapped. "Hold still." With a quick gesture, he jammed the root into my mouth and backed off, studying my face critically.

"Wh-what is it for?" I stammered.

"Big-game hunting," he returned loftily. I was screwing up my courage to inquire out of which end the bullet came when he suddenly plucked it from my teeth. "No, I don't care for you in that. Let's see now—what's your club?"

"Why—er—uh—the Williams After-Shave Club," I replied politely. "You know, for men whose skins welcome that zestful, bracing tang——"

"No, no," he broke in irritably. "Where do you keep your yacht?" His face darkened and he took a threatening step forward. "You have a yacht, haven't you?"

"Oh—why—er—bub—certainly," I lied skillfully. "He's—

I mean, she's laid up right now, the man's scraping her chimney. It got full of seaweeds."

Harkrider glared at me suspiciously, clearly unconvinced.

"Yo heave ho, blow the man down," I hummed nonchalantly, executing a few steps of the sailor's hornpipe. "Thar she blows and sparm at that! A double ration of plum duff for all hands, matey!" The stratagem was successful; with a baffled grunt, Harkrider produced a green velvet jewel case and exhibited a small, charred stub encrusted with salt.

"That's been used before, hasn't it?" I faltered.

"Of course it's been used," he grated. "You don't think you're going to get a new pipe for sixty-seven dollars, do you?"

"Oh, no, naturally," I agreed. "Tell you the truth, I had in mind something a bit smaller."

"Smaller?" snorted Harkrider. "You ought to have a calabash to go with that jaw of yours!"

"That's what I was telling the wife only this morning," I chuckled. "Gee, did you ever see anything like it? It's worse than an English bulldog's."

"Well, do you want a calabash or not?" he interrupted. "They're twenty dollars—though I guess you don't see that much money in a year, do you?" Blushing like a lovely long-stemmed American Beauty rose, I explained that I merely wanted something to knock around in, a homely old jimmy pipe I could suck on while dispensing salty aphorisms like Velvet Joe. After a heartrending plea, he finally consented to part with a factory second for thirteen dollars, equipped with an ingenious aluminum coil which conveyed the nicotine juice directly into the throat before it lost its potency. To prove my gratitude, I immediately bought a tobacco jar in the shape of a human skull, two pounds of Buntwell's Special Blend of chopped amethysts and attar of roses, and a cunning all-purpose reamer equally useful for removing carbon from a pipe or barnacles from a boat. Peeling eighty-three rugs from my skinny little roll, I caught up my purchases and coursed homeward whistling gems from *The Bartered Bride.* Right after dinner, I disposed myself in my favorite easy chair, lit a cheery blaze in the pipe and picked up the evening paper.

When I regained consciousness, there was a smell in the apartment like a Hindu suttee, and an angel in starched denim was taking my pulse and what remained of my roll. If I go on improving at this rate, she's promised I can get up tomorrow. That means I can go out Wednesday and go to pokey on Thursday, because in the meantime I've got a date to heave a brick through a plate-glass window in Radio City. See you around, bud.

Before and After

No mahogany-faced retired colonel of the Rajputana Rifles am I, rustling his morning *Times* and snorting indignantly. I never received a nasty sabre cut in the recent unpleasantness at Peshawar during the Sepoy Mutiny, and I do not live with my brother Thaddeus Sholto and a housekeeper in a trim little villa at No. 27, Maida Vale. On the contrary, I am a rather patient little gray-faced man who likes to sit with his feet propped against the oven, munching cookies and leafing through the works of Kirk Munro. My blood boils at a much higher point than Colonel Sholto's, but if I ever fall down foaming with an apoplectic stroke, I want you to run out and arrest the Hookless Fastener Company of Meadville, Pennsylvania. They may not be the actual culprits, but they'll know who did it.

The Hookless Fastener Company (there *can't* be a man named Mr. Hookless) sells a small patented device called the Talon Slide Fastener. This little novelty has been grafted onto men's trousers (I'm not repeating gossip; just look through almost any magazine). For some time the company has been conducting a campaign featuring a series of contrasting photographs. Two pictures of a young man, before and after streamlining, illustrate the manufacturer's contention that "millions of men, now wearing trousers tailored with Talon, will never go back to buttons again!"

My every good wish to the Hookless Fastener Company and their invention, which should prove more revolutionary than the cotton gin. The time is at hand when Yale upperclassmen will be saying sadly, "Yes, he banished unsightly film, all right, all right, but lack of Talon kept him out of Bones." What sets my pulses hammering, however, is the furtive horseplay Mr. Hookless and his associates resort to in their photographs. Just what *is* going on in that darkroom, fellows?

The last Talon advertisement I caught showed two photographs of a young man seated on a Jacobean stool, his right hand hooked into his vest pocket. In the first one, he was being very chipper and alert, in the way in which a man listens at the door of a Raines-law hotel. Mind you, I don't say the pictures were actually *taken* in a Raines-law hotel, but Mr. Goody Two-shoes managed to give that impression. In this photograph he wore the old-fashioned, or hangdog, trousers; in the other, he was styled by Talon. Otherwise the photographs were supposed to be identical.

But were they? I submit that they most emphatically were not. Before Talon, this young man wears a loose and foolish grin. Just a little too much pomade on his hair. No handkerchief in his breast pocket. You couldn't swear to it, but you get the feeling that he wears students' and misfit clothing—not because he has to, but because he rather enjoys it. The sort of young sneak who has plenty of pocket money (wheedled out of an infirm aunt, from whom he has expectations) but jots down his expenditures in a cheap shagreen notebook. There is even a vague air of kleptomania about him, and you are inclined to wonder what he is clutching so firmly in his vest pocket. A deck of heroin, possibly? A curious work called "Miss Birch's Secret"?

A lightning change into a pair of stylish trousers upholstered with Talon, a clove popped into the mouth to remove the scent of the cubebs he has been puffing, and what have we now? As mealy-mouthed a psalm-singing scoutmaster as you will meet in a day's hard riding. More sleek than best-quality Cloverdale butter, he sits with eyes rolled piously upward, waiting for Mr. Inskip to present him with the half-pound box of chocolate peppermints for perfect Sunday-school attendance. Oh, you dog!

What the Hookless Fastener people are selling, of course, is nothing as crass as zippers for pants, but spiritual regeneration, a commodity made famous by one Feodor Dostoevski about 1866. But where it took that certain party five hundred pages of pica type, an ax murder, some pretty creepy dreams, and a trip to the salt mines to bring Raskolnikov into line, the Talon boys do the trick in three minutes with a little sliding clamp. Commander Evangeline Booth and her girls had better stop shifting uncomfortably from one foot to the other and get down to realities. If that advertisement is any indication, a few valisefuls of these gadgets would make Gautama Buddha look like a prairie evangelist.

I'm afraid it will do very little good for the Hookless Fastener Company to come snivelling to me with *histoires* about elves getting into the engraving room and lousing up the detail. And they needn't think they can get saucy with me, either. They can put hired thugs on my trail, bomb my front porch, and steal my women, but they can't muzzle me. From now on I walk well in the middle of Seventh Avenue whenever I pass through the Garment Center. I may not look very chic with that cord tied around my middle to hold up my pants, but, by God, I still have my principles.

Hell in the Gabardines

AN OLD SUBSCRIBER of the *New Republic* am I, prudent, meditative, rigidly impartial. I am the man who reads those six-part exposés of the Southern utilities empire, savoring each dark peculation. Weekly I stroll the *couloirs* of the House and Senate with T.R.B., aghast at legislative folly. Every now and again I take issue in the correspondence pages with Kenneth Burke or Malcolm Cowley over a knotty point of aesthetics; my barbed and graceful letters counsel them to reread their Benedetto Croce. Tanned by two delightful weeks at lovely Camp Nitgedaiget, I learn twenty-nine languages by Linguaphone, sublet charming three-room apartments with gardens from May to October, send my children to the Ethical Culture School. Of an evening you can find me in a secluded corner of the White Turkey Town House, chuckling at Stark Young's review of the *Medea.* I smoke a pipe more frequently than not, sucking the match flame into the bowl with thoughtful little puffs.

Of all the specialists on that excellent journal of opinion, however, my favorite is Manny Farber, its motion-picture critic. Mr. Farber is a man zealous and incorruptible, a relentless foe of stereotypes, and an extremely subtle scholiast. If sufficiently aroused, he is likely to quote *The Cabinet of Dr. Caligari* four or five times in a single article (Mr. James Agee of the *Nation,* otherwise quite as profound, can quote it only once). It has been suggested by some that Mr. Farber's prose style is labyrinthine; they fidget as he picks up a complex sentence full of interlocking clauses and sends it rumbling down the alley. I do not share this view. With men who know rococo best, it's Farber two to one. Lulled by his Wagnerian rhythms, I snooze in my armchair, confident that the *mystique* of the talking picture is in capable hands.

It was in his most portentous vein that Mr. Farber recently sat himself down to chart the possibilities of the concealed camera. In transferring *The Lost Weekend* to the screen, you will recall, the producers sought verisimilitude by bringing Ray Milland to Third Avenue (in the past d Avenue had always been brought to Ray Milland) photographing the reactions of everyday citizens to Don Birnam's torment. The necessary equipment was hidden in theater marquees, "L" stations, and vans along the route of the historic trek, and almost nobody knew that the scenes were being registered on film. Mr. Farber heartily approved this technique and called on Hollywood to employ it more generally. To demonstrate its potentialities, he even sketched a wee scenario. "If," said he, "your plot called for some action inside of a department store, the normal activity of the store could be got by sending trained actors into it to carry on a planned business with an actor-clerk. Nobody else in the store need become conscious or self-conscious of this business, since the cameraman has been slyly concealed inside an ingeniously made store dummy and is recording everything from there."

Through a source I am not at liberty to reveal without violating medical confidence, I have come into possession of a diary which affords an interesting comment on Mr. Farber's idea. It was kept by one Leonard Flemister, formerly a clerk in the men's clothing section of Wanamaker's. I was not a customer of Flemister's, as I get my suits at a thrift shop named Sam's on the Bowery, but I had a nodding acquaintance with him; we often occupied adjoining tables at the Jumble Shop, and I remember him as a gentle, introspective man absorbed in the *New Republic* over his pecan waffle. He is at present living in seclusion (the Bonnie Brae is not a booby hatch in the old-fashioned sense) in New Jersey. I append several extracts from his diary:

JANUARY 12—Today rounds out seventeen years since I started in the men's shop at Wanamaker's, and they have been years filled with quiet satisfaction. As our great Founder constantly observed in his maxims, it is the small things that count. How truly this applies to ready-made suits! To the tyro, of course, one suit is very much like another, but to us who know, there is as much distinction between a Kuppenheimer and a Society Brand as there is between a Breughel and a Vermeer. Crusty old Thomas Carlyle knew it when he wrote *Sartor Resartus.* (Good notion, that; might pay me to keep a couple of his quotations on the tip of my tongue for some of our older customers.)

Ran into Frank Portnoy yesterday at lunch; haven't seen him since he left us for Finchley's. Sound enough chap on cheviots, is Frank, but I wouldn't care to entrust him with a saxony or tweeds. He seems to have put on five or six pounds in the seat, and I thought his 22-ounce basketweave a touch on the vulgar side. "Still working in that humdrum old place?" he asked, with a faint sneer. I kept my temper, merely remarking that he had incurred some criticism for leaving his position after only twelve years. (I did not bother to say that Mr. Witherspoon had referred to him as a grasshopper.) "Oh," he said airily, "I guess I learned enough of those lousy maxims." I said pointedly that he apparently had not learned the one about patience, and quoted it. He termed it "hogwash." "Maybe it is," I retorted, "but don't you wish you could wash a hog like that?" He turned as red as a beet and finished his meal in silence.

Read a disturbing article in the *New Republic* last night. A man named Farber advocates secreting cameramen inside clothing dummies in department stores so that the clerks may unwittingly become actors in a movie. Of course it was just a joke, but frankly, I thought it in rather poor taste.

January 14—Felt a trifle seedy today; I must find some other lunch spot besides the Green Unicorn. Their orange-and-pimento curry appears to have affected my digestion, or possibly I have had a surfeit of banana whip. In any case, during the afternoon I experienced the most extraordinary sensation, one that upset me considerably. At the rear of our sportswear section, next to the seersucker lounging robes, is a perfectly prosaic wax mannequin wearing a powder-blue ski jacket, canary-colored slacks, and synthetic elkskin loafers. About three o'clock I was hurrying past it with an armful of corduroy windbreakers when I heard a resounding sneeze. I turned abruptly, at first supposing it had come from a customer or salesperson, but the only one in sight was Sauerwein, who was absorbed in his booklet of maxims a good thirty feet away. Ridiculous as it may sound, the noise—a very distinct "Harooch!"—seemed to have emanated from the model. A moment's reflection would have told me that my auditory nerve was rebuking me for overindulgence at table, but unfortunately, in the first access of panic, I backed into a fishing-rod display and hooked a sinker in my trousers. Mr. Witherspoon, chancing by, observed (I thought with some coarseness) that I ought to get the lead out of my pants. Sauerwein, who loves to play the toady, laughed uproariously. I shall be on my guard with Sauerwein in future; I do not think he is quite sincere.

Saw a tiptop revival of *The Cabinet of Dr. Caligari* and *Potemkin* last night at the Fifth Avenue Playhouse; they are having their annual film festival. Enjoyed them both, though most of *Caligari* was run upside down and *Potemkin* broke in three places, necessitating a short wait. Next week they are beginning their annual *Potemkin* festival, to be followed by a revival of *The Cabinet of Dr. Caligari.* Always something unusual at the Fifth Avenue.

JANUARY 17—Mr. Witherspoon is a tyrant on occasion, but as the Founder says so pungently, give the devil his due; every so often the quality that made him floorwalker shines through. This morning, for example, a customer I recall seeing at some restaurant (the Jumble Shop, I believe) created a scene. He was a peppery little gnome named, I think, Pevelman or Pedelman, with shaggy eyebrows and the tonsure of a Franciscan father. I noticed him fidgeting around the low-priced shorts for a half hour or more, trying to attract a salesman, but Sauerwein was behind on his maxims and I was busy rearranging the windbreakers. At length he strode over to Mr. Witherspoon, scarlet with rage, and demanded, in an absurd falsetto, whether he might be waited on. Mr. Witherspoon was magnificent. He surveyed Pevelman up and down and snapped, "Don't you know there's a peace on?" The customer's face turned ashen and he withdrew, clawing at his collar. Old Witherspoon was in rare good humor all morning.

Slight dizzy spell this afternoon, nothing of consequence. I wonder if anything could be amiss with my hearing. Curiously enough, it is normal except in the immediate vicinity of the mannequin, where I hear a faint, sustained clicking as though some mechanism were grinding away. Coupled with this is the inescapable conviction that my every move is somehow being observed. Several times I stole up on the dummy, hoping to prove to myself that the clicking came from within, but it ceased instanter. Could I have contracted some mysterious tropical disease from handling too many vicuña coats?

Sauerwein is watching me. He suspects all is not well.

JANUARY 20—Something is definitely wrong with me. It has nothing to do with my stomach. I have gone mad. My stomach has driven me mad.

Whatever happens, I must not lose my head and blame my stomach. A stomach blamed is a stomach spurned, as the Founder says. The only good Founder is a dead Founder. Or Flounder. Now I *know* I am mad, writing that way about the Flounder.

I must marshal my thoughts very carefully, try to remember what happened. Shortly after one, I was alone in the department, Sauerwein and Witherspoon being at lunch. I was folding boys' windbreakers at the folded boys' windbreaker counter when a customer approached me. Never having seen Fredric March in person, I cannot assert dogmatically that it was he, but the resemblance was startling. From the outset, his behavior impressed me as erratic. He first struck a pose about fifteen feet from the mannequin, taking care to keep his profile to it. As he did so, the clicking sound which had harassed me became doubly magnified. Then, in the loud, artificial tone of one who wished to be overheard, he demanded to be shown a suit with two pairs of pants.

"We haven't any," I replied. "Don't you know there's a peace on?" To my surprise, he emitted a hoarse cry of delight and slapped his thigh.

"That'll be a wow!" he chortled. "We'll leave that line in!" Seventeen years of dealing with eccentrics have taught me the wisdom of humoring them; I pretended not to have heard. He gave me an intimate wink, snatched a sharkskin suit from the rack, and vanished into a dressing room. I was on the point of summoning aid when he reappeared feverishly. The effect of the trousers, at least three sizes too large for him, was so ludicrous that I stood speechless.

"Just what I wanted," he grinned, surveying himself in the mirror. Simultaneously, almost as if by prearrangement, a young lady in flamboyant theatrical make-up appeared. To my horror, the customer forgot to hold onto his trousers and they dropped down around his ankles. "Hello, Vivian!" he cried. "Well, I guess you caught me with my pants down!" And then—I am resolved to spare no detail—a voice from within the mannequin boomed *"Cut!"*

When I recovered consciousness in the dispensary, the nurse and Mr. Witherspoon were chafing my wrists and Sauerwein was whispering to a store detective. I seem to remember striking Sauerwein, though I also have the impression my hands were entangled in my sleeves. The rest I prefer to forget. It can be summed up in the word "nightmare." Nightmare.

FEBRUARY 5—It is very quiet here at Bonnie Brae and the food is excellent, if a little unrelieved. I could do with one of those tasty watercress-and-palmetto salads they know so well how to prepare at the Green Unicorn. The library here is well stocked with current magazines; I keep abreast of the news via the *New Republic,* though I confess Farber does not grip me as he used to.

I have only one objection to this place. In the library is a suit of medieval armor, and very often I could swear that a pair of eyes are watching me through the casque. As soon as the weather becomes warmer, I expect to spend most of my time on the piazza.

Let Sleeping Dogs Lie

ONE EVENING last week I was dreaming over a drawer full of old love letters, fancy rhinestone garters, and similar trophies of the chase when I turned up a fading snapshot depicting two coxcombs of the vintage of 1922. Against the unlovely façade of the Brown University chapel, the photographer had immortalized my roommate and myself in an attitude recalling Damon and Pythias. We both wore green Norfolk jackets and Tattersall waistcoats, clenched class pipes trimmed with numerals in our teeth, and generally suggested a couple of cynical, fatigued rips who knew a from a handsaw. I was suddenly suffused with a warm, zy emotion and the sensation that a tennis ball had dged in my larynx. Tears the size of Catawba grapes welled down my seamed cheeks; across the years I heard again the trumpet passage from "When Day Is Done" and the Mound City Blue Blowers in "Hindustan." Automatically, I reached for my hip, half expecting to find the curved and monogrammed flask filled with gin at body heat.

Trembling with emotion, I sought out my consort, a statuesque creature compounded of fire and ice. She was in the scullery, where she was compounding some fire and ice in a glass. I informed her I was arranging a reunion with old Jim Budlong, to whom I referred with a sob as the salt of the earth and a perfect crackajack. The prospect of listening to us exhume our student pranks, while she discussed dress patterns with a total stranger, naturally electrified her. Ducking the oncoming coffee grinder with the grace of a born athlete, I sauntered negligently to the phone and called the old crackajack.

On the appointed eve, the napery was flawless and my eyes outshone the silver service as I busily shook up Martinis with imported vermouth and opened a box of choicest Havanas. The dinner had hardly smoldered to a crisp before the old crackajack entered. Beyond acquiring a set of false teeth, a paunch and a slight facial paralysis, he had not changed a whit. His wife, a vinegary soubrette with rimless bifocals, straggled in, ten paces behind. The two ladies exchanged a limp handshake and sat down, eying each other venomously. With a hearty chuckle that sounded like a man strangling on a piece of bread, I whisked out the cocktails. It developed that our guests did not indulge, though Mrs. Budlong explained that if people wanted to make a pig of themselves, that was their own business. There was a short silence lasting twelve minutes during which the Czarina and I made pigs of ourselves.

When the pressure reached forty pounds to the square inch, I could stand it no longer.

"Hiya, old sock!" I roared out abruptly, pounding my classmate between the shoulder blades.

"Hiya, old keed!" he roared back, pounding my shoulder blades. This exhausted the subject and the four of us studied our palms minutely. At length, Mrs. Budlong leaned over and informed my wife, with sweet satisfaction, that her bra was showing.

"I know it," replied the latter through her teeth. "That's the way I like it. I think it's more provocative, don't you?" The Budlongs exchanged a glance indicating that their hostess was a blend of Messalina and Little Egypt.

"How long have you two been married?" demanded Mrs. Budlong, with the crisp aversion of a social worker.

"Why, we're not married!" my dream girl answered sunnily. "I thought you knew. He bought me down in Buenos Aires as a plaything. He's got a wife and three children up in Haverstraw."

As the maid kicked open the door to announce that the soup was on, a hush reminiscent of the Eden Musée greeted her. All we needed was a licensed mortician tiptoeing around placing pennies on our eyelids.

Dinner was a carnival of gaiety; Mrs. Budlong spent it furtively wiping the spoons to guard against infection, and her husband kept consulting his watch like a conductor on the Rock Island road. The boiled beef set his tongue wagging, however, and he made a little talk on steam turbines lasting into the *crepes suzette*. In desperation, I began harking back to youthful didos under the elms.

"Remember the time we hoisted the dean's cow up on the roof of the chem lab?" I giggled.

"Ho-ho, that was the cat's cuff links!" he chortled, turning excitedly to my wife. "Did he ever tell you about that one?"

"He did," snarled milady, "and I still say that if you could only put it up in tablets, you'd have the biggest thing since the discovery of chloroform."

At this juncture a world-famed surgeon named Al, who runs a small place on Third Avenue, telephoned that my grandfather was sinking fast at the Misericordia Hospital and was not expected to live through the floor show. We made a date with the Budlongs to take potluck in East Orange next Thursday, and sped like the wind to the bedside, but it was too late. Grandpa was deader than a mackerel—and that goes for a certain dinner date next Thursday, brother.

Nasal-happy Mamma, Don't You Try to Two-time Me

ONE DAY not long ago, idling through the pages of a sophisticated 35-cent monthly while waiting for the barber to give me my sophisticated 65-cent monthly haircut, I was suddenly oppressed by the characteristic shortness of breath, mingled with giddiness and general trepidation, that results whenever one gets too near an advertisement for Tabu. This exotic scent, in case you have been fortunate enough to forget it, is widely publicized as "the 'Forbidden' Perfume," which means, when all the meringue is sluiced away, that it is forbidden to anyone who doesn't have $18.50 for an ounce of it. The language used to describe Tabu is a chutney compounded of Pierre Loti and the Symbolist poets, so fiery that it sets every nerve aquiver, particularly those controlling the process of regurgitation. "Tabu," pants the copywriter, "a sultry, heady, lid-lowering fragrance that has whispered its way around the globe . . . intriguing as a suppressed book . . . exciting as a locked door . . . heady, sultry, confusing . . . smoulders for weeks on your gowns or furs, becoming more and more tantalizing all the while. In fact," he sniggers, leaning forward until his eyes become mere slits in his unattractive face, "until recently, Tabu came secretly from Abroad." This tender confidence appears to me romantic but somewhat unguarded; when I was a débutante, the United States Customs had pronounced views about smuggling contraband in your girdle.

The rhapsodic text of the advertisement, however, is mere frosting for its art work, which I assume is an attempt to crystallize the elusive quality of Tabu. Two citizens in evening dress, engaged in a refined musicale, have apparently experienced a common libidinal drive and fused in a fierce embrace before a piano. The ardor of the pair is well-nigh volcanic. The gentleman's hair cascades down his forehead and he holds a violin at arm's length as though to pulverize it in his fingers; the lady, her wrists trailing the piano keys, is bent backward in an arc recalling the Camel Walk of 1922. It seems a pity that the Tabu people, while they were so busy stirring the senses, could not have provided some slight clue to a glamorous situation. What provoked it? Had a drop of the sultry, lid-lowering essence whispered its way around the young woman's corsage, ultimately driving her cavalier to distraction? Or is the caress itself taboo for some undisclosed reason? In fine, I resent being inflamed by a pack of upstart perfumers. They play the coquette in the taxicab and, once in the foyer, twist out of my grasp with a casual "Well, call me up soon, won't you, dear boy?"

In an effort to reduce my blood pressure, but always retaining a spirit of stern scientific inquiry, I submit the following a-priori explanation of the circumstances. Anyone interested in the amateur rights of this harlequinade, for production at schools and churches, should have his head examined.

[*Scene: A suburban living room on the Main Line. As the curtain rises, Mavis Huntoon, thirty-three and disillusioned, sits at her Bechstein playing a Chopin étude. Robin Huntoon, a stolid, unimaginative man of forty who lives only for hardware, is seated in a Sleepy Hollow chair fondling some screws and hinges. After a moment, Mavis rises restlessly and moves to the French windows at rear.*]

MAVIS (*wistfully*): It's raining again.

ROBIN: Forty-five thousand, three hundred and eleven . . . forty-five thousand, three hundred and twelve . . .

MAVIS: What are you doing?

ROBIN: I'm counting my money. (*With an involuntary*

shudder of disgust, Mavis picks up a limp-leather volume.)

MAVIS (*reading*):

O swallow, sister, O fleeting swallow,
My heart in me is a molten ember
And over my head the waves have met.

ROBIN: Hot spit. What's that?

MAVIS (*wearily*): You wouldn't understand. It's Swinburne.

ROBIN: Swinburne? I knew a Nate Swinburne once. He ran a hardware store in Mystic, Connecticut. . . . Why, what's the matter?

MAVIS (*with a strangled sob*): I can't stand it! I'm stifling here!

ROBIN: It *is* kind of close, now you mention it. I'll open a window.

MAVIS (*coming up close to him*): Robin, don't you notice anything different about me?

ROBIN (*sniffing*): Hm-m-m. Why, yes, you've got a funny smell.

MAVIS: Don't you find me heady, sultry, confusing?

ROBIN: No. (*Critically*) But you've put on a lot of weight lately.

MAVIS: Have I?

ROBIN: You certainly have. You're as big as a house. And your slip is showing.

MAVIS: I'm not wearing a slip.

ROBIN: Well, it would show if you were.

MAVIS: Anything else?

ROBIN: Maybe I shouldn't call attention to it.

MAVIS: No, no, darling. By all means call attention to it.

ROBIN: You're getting wrinkles under the eyes. And a scraggly neck, like a turkey.

MAVIS: Not much gets past you, does it?

ROBIN (*comfortably*): I guess I'm just about as wide awake as anybody in the hardware business.

MAVIS: Well, look again. You've missed something.

ROBIN (*starting*): Why, you're holding a little gun.

MAVIS: Aha. And now I pull back this gadget on top.

ROBIN: What are you doing that for?

MAVIS: We call it "fanning back the hammer." (*She drills Robin neatly between the eyes. As she breaks the breech and thoughtfully extracts the shell, the doorbell sounds. With a moue of distaste, Mavis takes Robin by the necktie and rolls him behind the davenport. Then, applying a hint of Tabu to her lobes, she crosses to the door. Locksley Mendoza enters, wrapped in an Inverness cape. His handsome face is lean, coolly ironic, bronzed by tropical suns. As Mavis moves wordlessly to her Bechstein, Mendoza whips out a priceless Amati from its case and they launch into Jocelyn's "Berceuse." Suddenly a harsh oath escapes his lips; he drops the bow, seizes Mavis in a grip of wool.*)

MENDOZA: *Sapristi!* You turn a man's bones to water inside his skin, you she-devil.

MAVIS (*struggling*): Oh, my very dear, you can't—you mustn't. It is "taboo."

MENDOZA: "Taboo"? When two people are loving each

other until the seams are coming apart in the clothes, it is "taboo"?

MAVIS: No, no, it cannot be.

MENDOZA (*hoarsely*): I tell you the blood is boiling in my veins! You are a candy store filled with luscious nougats, a henhouse from which the pullets have yet to be stolen!

MAVIS: Promise me one thing. Whatever happens—whatever they should tell you about me—we'll always have this moment together.

MENDOZA: *Parbleu!* Do you think I am a milksap, that you can put me off with your bobbery? What stands between us—this man's foot sticking out from behind the davenport?

MAVIS: Of course not. It's—well—it's that you're not the man I thought you were. Who are you, anyway?

MENDOZA (*simply*): The exterminator.

MAVIS: Then why the violin?

MENDOZA: Just an attention-getter. Nowadays you got to dramatize yourself. (*Extracting a pasteboard box*) Can I interest you in our new brand of bedbug powder? It's a ripsnorter.

MAVIS (*sadly*): I think not. After all, *mon vieux,* in a sense we're competitors.

MENDOZA: But how?

MAVIS (*gently*): You see, darling, I'm something of an exterminator myself. (*As she produces her heater and fans back the hammer a second time.*)

CURTAIN

White Bimbo, or, Through Dullest Africa with Three Sleepy People

TAKE ONE THING with another, there are few places I know better than the heart of Africa. Set me down in Bechuanaland or the Cameroons and I will find my way home with less difficulty than I would from Rittenhouse Square or Boylston Street. My entire youth, in a sense, was spent on the Dark Continent. By the time I was eleven, I was probably the world's foremost authority on the works of Sir H. Rider Haggard, or at least the foremost eleven-year-old authority in Providence, Rhode Island. My impersonation of Allan Quatermain tracking down a spoor was so exact and so forthright that a popular movement sprang up among my fellow-citizens to send me to Mombasa. I was, however, not quite ready for Mombasa and begged off. At fifteen, I could quote Livingstone and Paul Du Chaillu so glibly that my sponsors revived their project, this time offering to send me to Tanganyika. It became sort of a good-humored tug of war to get me out of New England. I don't want to sound chesty, but I suppose I've done more harm to Africa in my day than Cecil Rhodes.

It came as a pang, therefore, to learn that my achievement had been overshadowed by that of a complete unknown, a person whose name occurs in no encyclopedia or reference work on Africa. Armand Brigaud may well be a familiar figure in the Explorers Club, and he can probably be found any afternoon at the National Geographic Society swapping yarns with William Beebe and Burton Holmes. Frankly, I never heard of him until yesterday, when I picked up a yellowing copy of a pulp magazine called *Jungle Stories* and read his novelette, *Killers on Safari.* Though it costs me an effort, I shall give the man his due. In *Killers on Safari,* Armand Brigaud has written finis to the subject of Africa. After him, the deluge. Me, I'll have a double deluge with very little soda, please.

To be quite candid, the safari the author celebrates in his title is about as exciting as a streetcar journey from New

Haven to Savin Rock, and his flora and fauna suggest the lobby display accompanying a Monogram jungle film. What lifts *Killers on Safari* from the ruck is a cast of characters out of Daisy Ashford by Fenimore Cooper, with Superman acting as accoucheur. Their adventures are recorded in some of the most stylish prose to flow out of an inkwell since Helen Hunt Jackson's *Ramona*. The people of Mr. Brigaud's piece, beset by hostile aborigines, snakes, and blackwater fever, converse with almost unbearable elegance, rolling out their periods like Edmund Burke. Here, for example, Diana Patten and Walter Huntley, a couple of the characters, in a sylvan glade, as their porters take a short breather:

"A coarse forest pig shuffled out of a ravine and began nibbling on a bamboo root. The shapely hand of Diana Patten made a gesture which encompassed the whole scene as she said softly: 'These beasts of the wilderness know when it is safe for them to come near the most murderous of all mammals: man!' Walter Huntley stared adoringly at her symmetrical features, which became so girlish and gentle when her red lips parted in a smile. For the thousandth time he thought that she was unusually tall, but breathtakingly gorgeous, from her wavy blonde hair down her statuesque body to her shapely feet. The big pig trotted back into the ravine."

This tropical idyll pauses for approximately twelve hundred words of exposition to establish Diana's and Walter's identity, and then:

"The forest hog emerged again from the ravine, leading a sow and four piglets. 'Are they not coarse, rough, and as perfectly alike as rain drops in every detail excepting size?' Diana chuckled, snuggling against Walter's shoulder." I cannot recall a more engaging passage in fiction, and I've been trying for almost eighteen seconds.

The principals of *Killers on Safari* are three: Dr. Hargrave, a goatish New York physician travelling through Sierra Leone on a scientific mission vaguely related to rejuvenation; Walter Huntley, his guide, a former patron of alcoholic beverages, seeking salvation; and Diana Patten, the doctor's nurse. Judged by ordinary hospital standards, Diana is the least conventional nurse ever sent out by a registry. The decorative heading represents her as a toothsome showgirl, clad in a minute swath of rayon and transfixing a gigantic black warrior with an assagai. "As a student in a women's college, she had won prizes in archery and javelin-throwing contests," Mr. Brigaud fluently explains. Diana, in all justice, has her softer side; somewhat later, when she and Walter are rushed by a savage, she cries out instinctively, "Don't kill him, but put a bullet into one of his legs!" Diana's innate sentimentality continually gets in her way; further on, a black chieftain named Wambogo invites her to share his pallet and she taunts him into duelling with javelins, with this result: "It would have been easy for her to disembowel Wambogo before the latter could bring his own spear into play. But she preferred to maim him. . . . Therefore she split open Wambogo's breast muscles, and cut his tendons under his armpit. Then, as he howled with pain and rage, she slid out of his grasp, leaped back, and pinked him through a leg." Lucky for Wambogo that Diana was only pettish, or she might really have unsheathed her claws.

The story opens with Diana warning Walter that their employer, Dr. Hargrave, has become jealous of their attachment and means him no good. Her apprehensions are justified, for the Doctor is everlastingly crouched in the shrubbery, tremulous with desire, cooking up schemes for eliminating the guide. At length he eggs on a treacherous native named Itira Nlembi to ambush Walter, but the latter draws first claret and the aggressor slinks off into the potted palms with the equivalent of a broken neck. The party now proceeds sluggishly to the territory of a tribe of fierce hall-boys called the Amutu, where Dr. Hargrave divides his time between healing the sick and pinching Diana. She finds his attentions odious and haughtily terms him a boor. Dr. Hargrave smarts under the insult:

"'So I am called a boor!' he mouthed angrily. 'I begin to have enough of your sponsoring the cause of the former tramp, Miss Patten!' And turning on his heels, he strode furiously toward the central pavilion. . . . When the portly bulk of Hargrave disappeared behind the lap [*sic*] of the pavilion acting as a door, her spirits sank and she moaned: 'From bad to worse! It is bad, very bad, to be under orders of a man on the verge of insanity! I wonder how it will all end!' " It all ends quite spiritedly, with Hargrave putting a slug in the guide's ribs and Walter bringing his revolver butt down on the Doctor's skull. This surprisingly restores good-fellowship all around, and the rivals unite to repulse an attack by the Amutu. Hargrave herewith exits untidily from the plot, struck down by a battle ax, but thanks to a homemade avalanche and some fast spear work by Diana, Walter and the girl get clear. It then transpires how foresighted Diana was to major in archery at college; she keeps the larder well stocked with antelope meat and liquidates a black leopard who waylays her in the greenery. Some index of her pluck on this occasion may be gained from Walter's words following the event:

" 'You acted with amazing spunk and skill. You are a marvelous heroine. But, damn it! For a moment I nearly got a stroke at the thought that that awful lion was about to tear you to shreds!' " He implores Diana not to go hunting unescorted in future, but, womanlike, she disregards him and sallies forth. Thereupon her lover behaves much in the manner of a Keystone two-reeler: "Walter tore his hat from his head, slammed it on the ground, and kicked it." Whether he jumped up and down on it or flung a custard pie after her is not indicated. His blood pressure again starts vaulting when a courier reports that Diana has been taken captive by Itira Nlembi: "Walter saw blood on his face, and on one of his arms, and almost got a stroke." Walter, in fact, constantly appears to be hovering on the edge of a syncope; the next time he sees Diana, in Itira's lair, he reacts characteristically: "Walter nearly became apoplectic at the sight of her dishevelled hair, bruised arms, and torn clothes." My knowledge of hypertension is elementary, but it seems to me Walter would be far better off rocking on the porch of a New Jersey milk farm than mousing around Sierra Leone.

The story (for want of a better term) now develops what is unquestionably the teeniest crescendo in the annals of modern typesetting. Itira Nlembi, overcome by Diana's charms, offers to make her his queen. Diana responds in her usual polished forensic style: "'I have been waiting for some hare-brained proposals ever since your evil-smelling grub-eaters ambushed and overcame me by sheer strength of numbers!'" Nevertheless, playing for time, she pretends to accede on condition that he court her for two months, as befits a lady of rank. Itira, anxious not to breach the rules of etiquette, assents. Then, aided by two ladies of the harem, the lovers vamoose and race to meet a British relief column they have magically notified. Itira's hatchetmen, of course, give pursuit. At the couple's darkest hour, just as Walter's arteries are snapping like pipestems, comes deliverance: "Walter's calm voice was belied by the feverish look of his eyes and his twitching lips. Suddenly he beamed ecstatically and shouted at the top of his lungs: 'Oh, my dear, there will be no reason of hurting that pretty head of yours! Look down there, toward the north! Don't you see gun barrels gleaming under the sun? They are coming, the British!'" A few rounds of grape disperse the blacks, and the British officer in command benignly advises Walter and Diana to get themselves to the nearest chaplain. " 'And,' he adds, with a gruff chuckle, 'could I be best man? I sort of think it would round up my memories of this chapter of adventures spiced by human interest.' "

And so, as apoplexy and archery join lips under the giant clichés and Kipling spins in his grave like a lathe, let us bid adieu to Armand Brigaud, a great kid and a great story teller. Dig you around Lake Chad, old boy, and don't take any wooden rhetoric.

So Little Time Marches On

Marquand's principal contact with Hollywood was in 1941, when *H. M. Pulham, Esquire* was produced by King Vidor for M-G-M and Marquand went to the Coast to work on the dialog. On Dec. 4, 1941 the film was released at a dual "world première" in Loew's State and Loew's Tremont Theaters in Boston. . . . Marquand was rushed around from one press conference to another and photographed wearing a sad smile as he presented to a Harvard librarian the original movie script. Marquand got back to New York from the world première with a slight cold and a nervous feeling that something drastic was about to happen. Two days later the Japanese attacked Pearl Harbor.—*From Roger Butterfield's biography of J. P. Marquand in* Life.

Out of these things, and many more, is woven the warp and woof of my childhood memory: the dappled sunlight on the great lawns of Chowderhead, our summer estate at

Newport, the bitter-sweet fragrance of stranded eels at low tide, the alcoholic breath of a clubman wafted on the breeze from Bailey's Beach. That my family was fantastically wealthy I was early aware, although good taste naturally forbade any excessive display. My father occasionally appeared at table in sack suits checkered with dollar signs, and the gardeners used rubies instead of gravel on the paths, but the guest who so far forgot himself as to exclaim "Hot puppies!" and fill his pockets with the baubles was rarely invited again. One of my first distinct recollections is of watching the men burn leaves under the giant elms and my momentary surprise when I found that they were not leaves but old banknotes. I felt then, with the kind of intuition children alone know, that my lot would be different from that of my fellows.

Almost from the moment of birth, it seems to me, I was passionately fond of books; before I was quite five, I devoured in a single afternoon Doughty's *Arabia Deserta,* the Pandects of Justinian (in translation, of course), and the novels of Mrs. Aphra Behn, a piece of gluttony that ultimately involved the services of three stomach specialists from the Massachusetts General Hospital. It was this youthful predilection for belles lettres that first brought me into conflict with my father. He had been reading *The Private Papers of Henry Ryecroft* and had mislaid it. Fearful lest I might have eaten it, he invaded the nursery and demanded, "Have you noticed any Gissing around here?" "No, sir," I replied submissively, "but I saw you pinching Nannie in the linen closet." He frowned thoughtfully and withdrew, leaving me prey to a strange uneasiness. Four days later, Italy declared war on Tripoli.

Though life at Chowderhead was spacious, to say the least, my father did not believe in pampering the young, and constantly strove to imbue in me a sense of frugality. Until I was eight, I received an allowance of five cents a month, for which I was held strictly accountable. Of course, five cents in those days bought a good deal more than it does now; it bought a firkin of gherkins or a ramekin of fescue or a pipkin of halvah, but since I was expected to furnish my own clothes out of this sum, I had little left for luxuries. I well recall my bitterness when I discovered that the small hoard of pennies I had accumulated over the summer was missing from my knickerbockers. There had been a series of minor peculations at home that year and I suspected the housekeeper's son, a rather ferret-faced lad. I wrung a confession from him, and, to teach the pickpocket a lesson, plunged his head repeatedly into the bay. As luck would have it, my father happened along at this juncture. His jaw dropped. "What are you doing there, young man?" he snapped. "Well, guv'nor," I chuckled, "I guess you might say I was taking a little dip in the ocean." Retrieving his jaw, my father continued his constitutional with a glance that boded me no good. Nine days later, Bosnia severed relations with Herzegovina.

If my father prided himself on anything, it was his unconventional theories about education. To him the customary progression from the grammar grades through high school to college was so much poppycock. Consequently, when I was eight, I was apprenticed to the proprietor of a delicatessen store in Portland, Maine, to acquire worldly experience before entering a university. The nine exciting years I spent under the tutelage of genial Ned Harnischfeger did more to mold my character than anything I could possibly imagine. As I wrapped a succulent cut of smoked salmon for a customer, Ned would painstakingly describe the topography of Nova Scotia, the tides in the Bay of Fundy, and the dynamics of spawning; a corned-beef sandwich on rye was a handy pretext for a lecture on domestic cattle, cereal grains, or the general subject of indigestion. My Portland phase terminated in a curious fashion. One noon I was busily filling orders behind the counter. Suddenly, out of the corner of my eye, I saw Grimalkin, our mouser, leap upon a table, seize a customer's lunch, and bolt out into the alley. The customer, thunderstruck, stammered forth some inarticulate comment. "What's the matter, stupid?" I demanded roughly. "Has the cat got your tongue sandwich?" He went scarlet. I saw Harnischfeger's lips tighten and I knew subconsciously that a turning point in my life was at hand. Two days later, Georges Carpentier climbed into the ring at Boyle's Thirty Acres and I entered Harvard.

From the beginning I was recognized as a leader in my

class, one of the few whose destiny it is to inspire and guide their less gifted mates. (I often say that college is a microcosm, a tiny world in which is foreshadowed the turbulence of actual life. That is what I often say.) My freshman year, unluckily, was marred by family dissension. Unbeknownst to me, violent quarrels were raging at home, my mother accusing my father of pettiness and cupidity. At last she could abide his stinginess no longer and departed for Reno. The news reached me, oddly enough, during a French class, as we were translating an absorbing passage of Erckmann-Chatrian. His face grave, the instructor halted the lesson and read aloud a curt message stating that my mother had left home because of my father's avarice. "I hope this isn't too much of a shock, old man," he said sympathetically. "No, that's the way of the world," I replied. "Money makes the *mère* go." An expression I could not fathom clouded the instructor's face and I was oppressed by a vague sense of disaster. Three days later a society bridge expert named Joseph B. Elwell padded downstairs with a sleepy yawn, bringing an era to a close.

It would be both immodest and redundant to detail the triumphs I scored in the balance of my stay at Cambridge. Suffice it to say that I won what paltry distinctions the gridiron, the diamond, and the debating platform could afford, not to mention completing the usual academic course in two and a half years. In one single instance did I come off second best, and then because I disdained to take unfair advantage of a rival in love. The latter was an immensely rich young Corsican upperclassman whose successes with the opposite sex were well-nigh as spectacular as my own. On the surface my relations with César Sporchini were friendly. We often sent each other a dancing girl or a dozen of Imperial Tokay, but we both knew who would be victor if our blades crossed. One evening, at the Old Howard Burlesque, we were both smitten with the same pair of captivating blue eyes. I subsequently persuaded their owner to share a cozy lobster-and-champagne supper in a private dining room at Locke Ober's. Despite the fabulous string of pearls I slyly insinuated under her plate, the silly creature remained obdurate. Again and again, in the weeks that followed, I plied her with gifts, only to discover that Sporchini was outbidding me for her favor. The Homeric struggle that ensued is still a legend in the chop houses along Scollay Square. At length, sacrificing heaven knows what vineyards and olive groves, Sporchini presented the fair tyrant with a solid-gold Stutz Bearcat and she yielded up her tawdry charms. I received word that I had been worsted with a philosophical shrug. "Oh, well," I observed, brushing a nascent mustache with my pinkie in the manner of the late Lew Cody, "money makes the Margot." My roommate stiffened and emitted a cryptic grunt that somehow filled me with anxiety. Five days later, Harry C. Klemfuss, the press agent for Campbell's Funeral Home, formally announced the passing of Rodolpho Alfonzo Raffaelo Pierre Filibert Guglielmi di Valentina d'Antonguolla, better known as "Rudy" Valentino.

The strident note of a distant banjo was stilled, the echo of undergraduate voices in the corridors hushed at last. It was time for me to face stern realities, to take over the reins of my father's vast industrial empire. Yet somehow I hungered for a creative outlet instead of the sordid money grubbing that awaited me. Acting on impulse at the eleventh hour, I joined a strolling Shakespearean troupe. For a time I was a mere supernumerary and fourth assistant stage manager. Then a dazzling stroke of fortune presented a chance to play a really important role. On the afternoon we were to give *Othello,* the leading man demanded an increase in salary. Denied it, he resigned in a temper. Shortly afterward, I encountered our impresario seated in the darkened auditorium, head buried in his hands. "I picked him up from the gutter!" he wailed. "I don't understand it!" "It's simple enough," I comforted him. "Money makes the Moor go." He looked up sharply and there was a challenge in his eyes that set my heart racing. One day later, Frances "Peaches" Browning sued for divorce and my theatrical career was a thing of the past.

And there, on the very threshold of life, face to face with the rich, dark promise of the years that lay ahead, let us leave me. Except for the beauty of Apollo and the mind of a Jesuit, I had scant equipment for the struggle: a trifling million or two in tax-free bonds, a leaky old yacht, a great, drafty mansion on Fifth Avenue peopled by ghosts. The Turgid Thirties were dawning, bringing with them the depression, Henry Luce, and, above all, the outsize picture magazine. A sense of prophecy was not enough. From now on I must learn how to duck.

Dental or Mental, I Say It's Spinach

A FEW DAYS AGO, under the heading, MAN LEAPS OUT WINDOW AS DENTIST GETS FORCEPS, *The New York Times* reported the unusual case of a man who leaped out a window as the dentist got the forceps. Briefly, the circumstances were these. A citizen in Staten Island tottered into a dental parlor and, indicating an aching molar, moaned, "It's killing me. You've got to pull it out." The dentist grinned like a Cheshire cat—*The New York Times* neglected to say so, but a Cheshire cat who was present at the time grinned like a dentist—and reached for his instruments. "There was a leap and a crash," continues the account. "The astonished dentist saw his patient spring through the closed window and drop ten feet to the sidewalk, where he lay dazed." The casualty was subsequently treated at a near-by hospital for abrasion and shock by Drs. J. G. Abrazian and Walter Shock, and then, like a worm, crept back to the dentist, apologized and offered to pay for the damage. On one point, however, he remained curiously adamant. He still has his tooth.

As a party who recently spent a whole morning with his knees braced against a dentist's chest, whimpering "Don't—don't—I'll do anything, but don't drill!" I am probably the only man in America equipped to sympathize with the poor devil. Ever since Nature presented me at birth with a set of thirty-two flawless little pearls of assorted sizes, I never once relaxed my vigilant stewardship of same. From the age of six onward, I constantly polished the enamel with peanut brittle, massaged the incisors twice daily with lollipops, and chewed taffy and chocolate-covered caramels faithfully to exercise the gums. As for consulting a dentist regularly, my punctuality practically amounted to a fetish. Every twelve years I would drop whatever I was doing and allow wild Caucasian ponies to drag me to a reputable orthodontist. I guess you might say I was hipped on the subject of dental care.

When, therefore, I inadvertently stubbed a tooth on a submerged cherry in an old-fashioned last week and my toupee ricocheted off the ceiling, I felt both dismayed and betrayed. By eleven the next morning, I was seated in the antechamber of one Russell Pipgrass, D.D.S., limply holding a copy of the *National Geographic* upside down and pretending to be absorbed in Magyar folkways. Through the door communicating with the arena throbbed a thin, bloodcurdling whine like a circular saw biting into a green plank. Suddenly an ear-splitting shriek rose above it, receding into a choked gurgle. I nonchalantly tapped out my cigarette in my eardrum and leaned over to the nurse, a Medusa type with serpents writhing out from under her prim white coif.

"Ah—er—pardon me," I observed, swallowing a bit of emery paper I had been chewing. "Did you hear anything just then?"

"Why, no," she replied, primly tucking back a snake under her cap. "What do you mean?"

"A—kind of a scratchy sound," I faltered.

"Oh, that," she sniffed carelessly. "Impacted wisdom tooth. We have to go in through the skull for those, you know." Murmuring some inconsequential excuse about lunching with a man in Sandusky, Ohio, I dropped to the floor and was creeping toward the corridor on all fours when Doctor Pipgrass emerged, rubbing his hands. "Well, here's an unexpected windfall!" he cackled, his eyes gleaming with cupidity. "Look out—slam the door on him!" Before I could dodge past, he pinioned me in a hammer lock and bore me, kicking and struggling, into his web. He was trying to wrestle me into the chair when the nurse raced in, brandishing a heavy glass ash tray.

"Here, hit him with this!" she panted.

"No, no, we mustn't bruise him," muttered Pipgrass. "Their relatives always ask a lot of silly questions." They finally made me comfy by strapping me into the chair with a half a dozen towels, tilted my feet up and pried open my teeth with a spoon. "Now then, where are his X-rays?" demanded the doctor.

"We haven't any," returned the nurse. "This is the first time he's been here."

"Well, bring me any X-rays," her employer barked. "What difference does it make? When you've seen one tooth, you've seen them all." He held up the X-rays against the light and examined them critically. "Well, friend, you're in a peck of trouble," he said at length. "You may as well know the worst. These are the teeth of an eighty-year-old man. You got here just in time." Plucking a horrendous nozzle from the rack, he shot compressed air down my gullet that sent me into a strangled paroxysm, and peered curiously at my inlays.

"Who put those in, a steamfitter?" he sneered. "You ought to be arrested for walking around with a job like that." He turned abruptly at the rustle of greenbacks and glared at his nurse. "See here, Miss Smedley, how many times have I told you not to count the patient's money in front of him? Take the wallet outside and go through it there." She nodded shamefacedly and slunk out. "That's the kind of thing that creates a bad impression on the layman," growled Doctor

Pipgrass, poking at my tongue with a sharp stick. "Now what seems to be the trouble in there?"

"Ong ong ong," I wheezed.

"H'm'm'm, a cleft palate," he mused. "Just as I feared. And you've got between four and five thousand cavities. While we're at it, I think we'd better tear out those lowers with a jackhammer and put in some nice expensive crowns. Excuse me." He quickly dialed a telephone number. "Is that you, Irene?" he asked. "Russell. Listen, on that white mink coat we were talking about at breakfast—go right ahead, I've changed my mind. . . . No, I'll tell you later. He's filthy with it."

"Look, doctor," I said with a casual yawn. "It's nothing really—just a funny tickling sensation in that rear tooth. I'll be back Tuesday—a year from Tuesday."

"Yes, yes," he interrupted, patting me reassuringly. "Don't be afraid now; this won't hurt a bit." With a slow, cunning smile, he produced from behind his back a hypodermic of the type used on brewery horses and, distending my lip, plunged it into the gum. The tip of my nose instantly froze, and my tongue took on the proportions of a bolt of flannel. I tried to cry out, but my larynx was out to lunch. Seizing the opportunity, Pipgrass snatched up his drill, took a firm purchase on my hair and teed off. A mixture of sensation roughly comparable to being alternately stilettoed and inflated with a bicycle pump overcame me; two thin wisps of smoke curled upward slowly from my ears. Fortunately, I had been schooled from boyhood to withstand pain without flinching, and beyond an occasional scream that rattled the windows, I bore myself with the stoicism of a red man. Scarcely ninety minutes later, Doctor Pipgrass thrust aside the drill, wiped his streaming forehead and shook the mass of protoplasm before him.

"Well, we're in the home stretch," he announced brightly, extracting a rubber sheet from a drawer. "We'll put this dam on you and fill her in a jiffy. You don't get claustrophobia, do you?"

"Wh-what's that?" I squeaked.

"Fear of being buried alive," he explained smoothly. "Kind of a stifling feeling. Your heart starts racing and you think you're going crazy. Pure imagination, of course." He pinned the rubber sheet over my face, slipped it over the tooth and left me alone with my thoughts. In less time than it takes to relate, I was a graduate member, *summa cum laude,* of the Claustrophobia Club. My face had turned a stunning shade of green, my heart was going like Big Ben, and a set of castanets in my knees was playing the "Malagueña." Summoning my last reserves of strength, I cast off my bonds and catapulted through the anteroom to freedom. I bequeathed Pipgrass a fleece-lined overcoat worth sixty-eight dollars, and he's welcome to it; I'll string along nicely with this big wad of chewing gum over my tooth. On me it looks good.

The Customer Is Always Wrong

I DARESAY that one of the strangest contradictions to beset contradiction fanciers recently was the situation confronting anybody who was seeking shelter in New York City. Not only were hotel rooms scarcer than the heath hen—after all, you *could* pick up an occasional heath hen before Christmas if you didn't mind going into the black market for it—but the reason for their scarcity was that most of them were occupied by people who had flocked to the National Hotel Exposition to discuss the scarcity of hotel rooms. Sounds paradoxical, doesn't it? I mean, if there aren't any other paradoxes around.

The National Hotel Exposition, it seems, is an annual powwow at which innkeepers forgather to discuss trade secrets: the maintenance of proper standards of insolence among room clerks, improved methods of juggling shower faucets so that guests are alternately frozen and parboiled, artful techniques for making windows stick, and the like. The chief topic of the convention, understandably, was overcrowding. A variety of speakers addressed the gathering, analyzing the congestion and suggesting remedies. The majority plumped for "good public relations" and similar shadowy panaceas, but one delegate from the City of Brotherly Love came out of his corner snarling. "The resident manager of the Warwick Hotel, in Philadelphia," stated the *Times*, "suggested a more selective method of meting out rooms . . . declaring himself in favor of the 'prestige guest who will be a source of revenue to the hotel,' adding that many long-term guests who are 'meaningless people' were cluttering up hotels and preventing them from gaining good prospects." This acid diagnosis was challenged from the floor (I use the term in its parliamentary sense; I would not wish to imply the gentleman was under the table) by an official of Chicago's Palmer House with the hot assertion that "the unimportant guest of today may be the 'big shot of tomorrow.' " The *Times* did not divulge the outcome of the spat, but I presume the principals invoked the code duello and pelted each other with Nesselrode pudding until the weaker cried uncle.

It so happens that several days ago I was privileged to see

the Chicagoan's philosophy dramatically vindicated before my very eyes in the lobby of the San Culotte, a rather dusty family hotel in the West Forties. I had gone there to meet a friend with whom I was lunching, Tom Pulsifer. Now Pulsifer is a good fellow (as a matter of fact, he is nothing of the sort; he is a mealy-mouthed sponger and a sneak), but he is never less than a half-hour late for appointments, and as I am invariably a half-hour early, I had oodles of time. I consumed a few by reading the *Sun* in its entirety, including such stop-press items as the news that Luna moths frequently attain a wing span of four inches and that the scup, or porgy, feeds on plankton. I don't know what it is about plankton that fascinates the *Sun's* make-up editor; he would rather run a good sparkling dispatch about plankton than the size of Nita Naldi's superstructure or some matter of genuine civic importance. Anyway, it set me wondering what Pulsifer, whose features are indistinguishable from those of a scup, would feed on, and borrowing a menu from a waiter, I worked out a series of light, nutritious salads and entrées I could gracefully direct to his attention. It was sheer boondoggling, I knew; he would inevitably start clamoring for canvasback and muscat grapes, and I would have to live out the month on salt cod to foot the bill. I had worked myself up into a very respectable fury at Pulsifer's gluttony and was about to phone him to cadge a meal from somebody else when I heard an irate voice behind me.

"Look at this lobby!" it was saying. "Did you ever see such a pack of crumbs? Of all the inconsequential, meaningless loafers—" I stole a glance over my shoulder and beheld a pursy, apoplectic gentleman, unmistakably the manager, surveying the lounge with arms akimbo. He was addressing a lathlike subordinate in mournful black and rimless bifocals, quite obviously his assistant.

"Shh, Mr. Leftwich," the younger man placated. "They're all steady guests, except one or two. Been here for years."

"You bet they have," snapped his superior. "That's what's wrong with the San Culotte. I tell you, Rightwich, I've had enough of these measly nonentities lousing up my establishment. I want people that *mean* something—celebrities, d'ye hear? Diplomats, movie stars, suave men of letters!"

"We had a suave man of letters last summer," reminded Rightwich, "but he left on account of the roaches."

"Listen," grated the manager. "I put thirteen thousand dollars' worth of roaches into this place to give it a homelike atmosphere, and anybody who doesn't like 'em can start packing!" He moved into my line of vision and indicated a commonplace citizen sleepily engaged in paring his nails. "Now, take that chump, for instance," he went on in a lower voice. "Who is he?"

"That's Mr. Detweiler," replied Rightwich. "He's an ideal guest. Never missed a bill. Why, he's so prompt—"

"Never mind that," interrupted Leftwich. "Promptness don't get you into *Who's Who*. What's he *do*?"

"Well," hesitated Rightwich, "he just sort of grooms his nails."

"You see?" snorted the other, triumphantly. "Dead wood. What I want is Humphrey Bogart sitting there grooming his nails, not a cipher named Detweiler. How about the one with the *Racing Form,* by the potted palm?"

"Mr. Pfannkuchen?" protested Rightwich, aggrieved. "Ah, gee, boss, he's gilt-edged—he pays us a year in advance. And he doesn't even ask for a room. He sleeps in a broom closet."

"He's a bottleneck," grunted Leftwich inexorably. "The place is full of 'em. That old lady knitting the afghan there—"

"She's kind of distinguished, though," appealed the assistant. "She looks like Dame May Whitty if you close your eyes a little."

"I'm closing my ears, too," growled Leftwich. "Get this straight, now. We're combing the small fry out of the register once and for all. I'll have public personalities like Jerome Zerbe and Choo Choo Johnson snoozing around this lobby or, by jiminy, I'll padlock the joint!"

"But gosh, Mr. Leftwich," implored the young man. "You can't tell, one of our guests *might* become famous all of a sudden. Every dog has his day."

"Just a minute," rapped the manager, wheeling on him. "Are you trying to take sides with the clientele?"

"No, no, of course not," stammered Rightwich, overcome with confusion. "All I mean is—"

"We've got an ugly name for that in our business, boy."

Leftwich's eyes had narrowed to mere slits. "It's called taking sides with the clientele."

"You know I wouldn't do a thing like that, sir," Rightwich pleaded.

"Well, I'm not so sure," his superior said suspiciously. "You worked at the Palmer House in Chicago, I seem to recall. If I hear any of that vicious Socialist twaddle about treating guests like human beings—"

"That was before I had my nervous breakdown," confessed Rightwich. "Oh, I know they're a lot of numskulls, but perhaps they're lucky, too. That girl sitting near the magazine stand with her mouth open might turn out to be another Jennifer Jones."

"She'd better work fast," retorted the manager, "because I'm going to screen the whole damn bunch right now. March 'em into the banquet room—and better pass out barrel staves to the help. They might turn nasty." Impervious to Rightwich's attempts to pacify him, Leftwich swung about and neatly caromed into a vital, incisive individual who had just entered the lobby. Before Leftwich could kick him, the newcomer whisked a briefcase from under his arm and unbuckled it.

"May I have your very kind attention for a moment, folks?" he asked in a ringing voice. The hum of chatter died away and heads turned inquisitively. Leftwich's dewlaps flushed scarlet.

"See here, Mac," he began. "We don't allow any pitchmen—"

"I beg your pardon," the stranger returned icily. "I'm Victor Robinette of Menafee, Soutache, Heppenstall & Preiselbeere, the advertising agency. Is there a Mr. Aubrey Detweiler here?"

"Why—er—yes," spoke up the dim man with the nail file. "That's me."

"Congrats, Mr. Detweiler!" boomed Robinette. "You've just been awarded first prize by the Invisible Mitten Corporation in their America's Most Expressive Hands Contest. Here is our check for ten thousand dollars." A spontaneous cheer burst from the throats of the assemblage, and well-wishers clustered about Detweiler, stroking his hands curiously and attempting to put the bite on him. Simultaneously, above the excited babble, the shrill pipe of a bellboy arrested the attention of all.

"Mr. Pfannkuchen, call for Mr. Dorian Pfannkuchen!" An overwrought lad in buttons threaded his way to the student of the *Racing Form*. "It's your bookmaker! You've won the daily double at Hialeah Park!"

"But the nags don't start running till three hours from now," objected Pfannkuchen, dumfounded.

"That's mere shilly-shallying," dismissed the boy, tumbling twenty-six thousand dollars in crisp greenbacks into his lap. "The fact remains that you are a veritable Monte Cristo, as sure as God made little green apples."

"Yes, and that's not all!" sang out Mrs. Roraback, the erstwhile anonymous knitter, jubilantly waving a money order in five figures. "A special-delivery screed from the

Albright Gallery in Buffalo informs me that they consider my last afghan an outstanding example of American folk art! Commissions are pouring in like herrings," she beamed, displaying sizable advance orders for throws, coverlets, and foot warmers. As flashlight bulbs exploded and newsreel cameramen jostled each other for advantage, Leftwich stood rooted to the spot, boiling with frustration.

"Try and cross me, will they?" he panted. "I'll get the spiteful creatures out of here if I have to burn the building down!" But fresh surprises still lay in store for him; two Hollywood directors, complete with megaphones, white riding breeches, and reversed linen caps, had appeared and were closely scrutinizing the girl near the magazine stand.

"She's dynamite!" the first murmured, awe-struck. "She's another Jennifer Jones!"

"You skimmed the words off my lips," assented the second. "I see her as Eppie in *Silas Marner,* or *The Mill on the Frost.*"

"No, I see her more as the scheming quadroon in *Pudd'nhead Wilson,*" his companion demurred.

"That's what I say," nodded the first. "She's versatile—she can play anything. Pact her!" In a trice, their discovery was signed to a seven-year contract, had had her hair restyled by Antoine, and, swathed in platina mink and orchids, was announcing her retirement from the screen to return to Broadway. Gloating unashamedly, Rightwich clapped his elder colleague on the back.

"Well, sir," he observed slyly, "this'll teach you not to go off half-cocked in future, ah?"

With a hoarse bellow, Leftwich struck his arm away. "I'll find *somebody* around here who's a no-account stooge!" he roared. His eyes darted about wildly and fastened on me. He extended an accusatory finger. "Who are you? What are you doing here?"

"Me? Why, nothing," I said automatically, and then caught myself at the indiscretion. "I—I mean, I've got a couple of diamond mines in the Rand, but please, I loathe publicity—"

"I knew it!" crackled Leftwich. "He's the one who's been cluttering up the building. Grab him, men!" In vain to protest that I was no guest of the house; rude hands seized my coat collar and frog-marched me toward the manager's office. Then, at the darkest hour, dawned deliverance. Through the revolving doors swept Tom Pulsifer—a Pulsifer reborn, a new authority in his bearing.

"Stop!" he thundered. "That man is my friend. Year in, year out, he has paid for my lunches, even when it meant denying himself luxuries and subsisting on soup greens. Now, thanks to the untimely demise of a crusty uncle in Australia, I can make belated restitution." And despite my most vigorous protestations, he stuffed my pockets with wad on wad of large-denomination currency. The discomfiture on Leftwich's countenance was comical in the extreme. Deferential to the point of servility, he fawned on us.

"Won't you stay and have lunch in my suite, gents?" he begged silkily. "I've a bottle of mellow Vouvray saved for just such an occasion."

"You have no suite, Leftwich," corrected Pulsifer in level tones. "On my way here, I bought the hotel and appointed Rightwich as manager in your stead. Let us hope that this has proved a salutary lesson to all."

"It has indeed," said the new manager, escorting us to the door as Leftwich was led away to become a dishwasher. "The next time you visit this fleabag, you will be greeted by a lobbyful of *schlemiehls* and nincompoops that will curl your hair." And with a genial wave, he placed his foot in the small of our backs and gave us a comradely shove into the stream of humanity eddying past the San Culotte.

A Child's Garden of Extroversion

ANYBODY WHO HAPPENED to be lounging on the sidewalk outside 1543 Broadway a week ago tonight could not have helped but notice a rather remarkable individual entering the music shop of O. Saporta at that address. Well over five feet in height, so exquisitely proportioned that he wrung a gasp of envy from the many lovers of exquisite proportions assembled there, his features blended poet, thinker, and man of action into a single harmonious whole. As light as a snowflake, as blithe as a bird, as black as ebony, as flat as a flounder, as busy as a bee, as dry as a reed, as lithe as a panther, as stout as an oak, and as clinging as a bur, he was followed and fawned upon by a troop of beggars, tumblers, performing bears, and women vying for his favor. Now and then, with a ducal wave, he flung largesse to all—a lakh of rupees, passes to Loew's State, a shower of gold-wrapped Whitman's chocolate wafers. At approximately nine-fifteen, he emerged from the shop with a neatly wrapped package, took a cab to my apartment, and lay down in my bed to read the book he had purchased. And there he remains, struck all of a heap and as dumb as an oyster.

How to Crash Tin-Pan Alley, says its title page, was "told by Arthur Jones to Louise Howard and Jeron Criswell," and published by Howard & Criswell, 12 West 44th Street, New York. If you think Noel Coward is versatile, you have yet to hear about Arthur Jones, Louise Howard, and Jeron Criswell. Co-author with Mr. Criswell of *How to Crash Broadway* and *How Your Play Can Crash Broadway*, Miss Howard will also be remembered for her novel, *Evasive Joy*. On page 35 of the Tin-Pan Alley book, a full-page photograph of the fair dynamo and her collaborator bears the caption, "The authors, Louise Howard and Jeron Criswell, with their composer, Arthur Jones, at the piano during an engagement." On page 72, leaning over a staff of music, are three views of "Louise Howard of the orchestra known as Louise Howard and her Gamboleers—Originator of Sophisticated-Primitive Music—authoress, composer, actress." The opposite page is given up to three views of "Arthur Jones of the orchestra known as Arthur Jones and his Jones Boys—Originator of Jumpy-Bumpy Music—author, composer, actor." Page 83 displays "Jeron Criswell—Playwright—Motion Picture and Broadway Producer—Actor-Manager" and reproduces a strip of film "from the motion picture *Span*, starring [ah, you peeked] Louise Howard, Arthur Jones and Jeron Criswell." (Though no clue is given, I presume it was produced at the West Coast studios of Criswell, Jones & Howard, shot with the new high-speed Criswell-Jones lens, and distributed by the Ho-Cris-Jo Exchange.) And just to make things complete, page 101 carries "Scenes from the Broadway Production of Oscar Wilde's *Life and Loves of Dorian Gray* taken on stage at the Comedy Theater, N.Y.C. Jeron Criswell was starred and heading the supporting cast were Louise Howard and Arthur Jones. The play was adapted by Mr. Criswell and the musical numbers 'I Was Just Around the Corner' and 'Victorian Waltz' were written by Miss Howard and Mr. Jones." How Oscar Wilde ever horned his way into the triumvirate must remain a mystery until the trio publishes its memoirs, which ought to be a week from Tuesday.

How to Crash Tin-Pan Alley begins with a short and glowing introduction by the *berühmte* jazz maestro Sammy Kaye (Swing and Sway). I have swung and swayed with Sammy Kaye for several years now, but our affair is at an end if he persists in being devoted to the first two-thirds of the book. It is presupposed that you have written a popular song, and forthwith you are carried through eighty-four pages of adventures with a set of Broadway characters named Mauvis Midnight, Horace Hamm, and Malcolm Doap IV which set the facial muscles aching with boredom. On page 103, the authors mercifully stop for wind and present a creed for song-writing success somewhat similar to the tenderfoot pledge of the Boy Scouts of America. One of its principal tenets is: "I keep my body free from dissipation and my mind clear and alert." I was not aware one had to take a physical examination to place a ballad with Shapiro, Bernstein & Co., but we live in a changing world.

It is not until the final chapter, just as the book starts to slip from your nerveless hand into the fire, that it really gets into the groove. The principles of conduct laid down in *Thirty Steps to Success!* as Arthur Jones told them to Louise Howard and Jeron Criswell tend to make Machiavelli seem a mealy-mouthed schoolboy by contrast. With the admonition "At no time be modest about your achievement," the authors outline a truly appalling program of self-exploitation. The successful song writer evidently must be a combination of Uriah Heep and Attila the Hun:

Start a scrapbook immediately. Save each newspaper clipping and each printed program that in any way mentions your name connected with your song. . . . Contact your local music store or stores and make arrangements for a full window display of your song, personally autographed copies. . . . Make personal appearances at clubs, high schools, churches, etc., giving your talk on songwriting. . . . On some "slow" evening at your local theater, convince the manager that your singers and yourself could comprise a complete vaudeville unit. Have your song thrown upon the screen and the audience sing it.

If the audience should be recalcitrant about singing, I imagine they can be clubbed into it. In addition, you are told to spend every spare moment wheedling and threatening "your local merchant" into printing your song on his advertising folders, chivying wardheelers into allowing you to appear at suppers and socials, and generally behaving like a yahoo. Since you will be travelling light and fast, the only ethics you will need are those indicated in Steps 5 and 16:

Always see that your singers are mentioned in your publicity because that is the only pay they will want.

It is important at this time to have people in your unit that are agreeable and who will work with you and not want pay for the present and who are able to pay their own expenses, and who will perform for the publicity and the fun of doing it.

Where you are going to pick up this collection of feebs and addlepates is no concern of the authors, who by Step 21 have made the following transition:

By this time you are a local, if not district, celebrity. Now is the time to make a definite approach to your local political representative who is now serving at the state capital. Show him your past clippings, programs and photographs, and tell him that you are his political ally, etc. . . . In fact, you have known all along that you were going to use this man and in a roundabout way you could have kept him informed of your rise so far, so that when you do approach him you are not unknown to him.

I presume that if you cannot "contact" this gentleman in his office, you can invade his bathroom and drag him out of the shower. Or, failing all else, he can always be trapped in a hotel room with a blonde.

Once you have run him to earth, however, the rest is pie. "Have this politician personally escort you to a booking agent for orchestras and musical entertainment," instructs Step 22, "and see to it that you are given a booking where you will be paid." At this stage the authors pause to consider the possibility that a stone may get into your shoe. "Whenever you meet blatant opposition [I love this use of the word 'blatant'] shrug your shoulders and try the next in line. You are now the pride of the state." And finally, says Step 30, "You have proven your ability to cope with all situations and by this time you are ready to receive your just reward." Which, Miss Howard and the Messrs. Criswell and Jones negligently forgot to add, should consist of two hundred lashes laid on with a blacksnake whip by your father. In case he tires, any other member of the family will be glad to spell him. And should they *all* happen to be out of town, just get in touch with me. I'll be only too happy to oblige.

En Garde, Messieurs! Change Your Oil?

IF I LIVE to be a hundred, an eventuality which may not concern you though it has set plenty of life insurance actuaries to biting their nails, I shall never forget the first time I encountered the Los Angeles *Times*. I don't remember what the paper was wearing, but I had on Fruit-of-the-Loom pajamas and I was leaning out of a compartment on a train as it stood panting in the station at Needles, California. It is hardly vital to this narrative that my hair was trimmed rather low in back, parted on the left side, and brushed straight back; I mention it only because it became something of a ford later on. Well, as I say, I leaned out and called to my porter, Cudgo, who was pilfering a piece of ice from the Atchison, Topeka, & Santa Fe for his julep. "Get me a newspaper, will you, dear?" Dear was slightly hard of hearing, and as a consequence I got the Los Angeles *Times*. When I arrived in Hollywood, another and a sorrier story, I found that the *Times* shared the morning field with a Hearst paper named the *Herald-Examiner*. I then made what is called "Hobson's Choice" after an ostler by the name of Hobson who also worked in a stable, and took the *Times* for several years. On the whole, I managed to get fairly adequate coverage of the news, with such minor omissions as the abdication of Alfonso and the Munich crisis, which had the bad luck to open against the Santa Ana Baby Parade. Precious beyond rubies, however, were the advertising columns, and from them, forty fathoms deep and factory fresh, came some perfect beauties to my table. Was I interested in high colonics, lessons in brain breathing, a darling chicken ranch in San Ysidro? Pack mules for transporting silver, a Cad. conv. cabr. steal at $485, a friendly fever to allay my gout, asthma, sciatica? Or perhaps something a little more ambitious—say, a partnership in Standard Oil?

Yes, lady, you wouldn't think so to look at these rags and this greasy old hat, but I am the partner of Rockefellers and Archbolds, and I have the advertisement to prove it. It was inserted by the Standard Oil Company of California and was charged with that tradition of camaraderie for the public which demands that billion-dollar corporations kick up their heels like colts in a pasture. "HO, ATHOS, PORTHOS!—YOU LIVE AGAIN," it sang. "Not alone for themselves did the Three Musketeers maintain their famed slogan of 'One for all and all for one.' When D'Artagnan came along upon his yellow horse they extended their fraternity to include him. In the spirit of Athos, Porthos, and Aramis, the oil companies of the Pacific Coast have achieved in common an uncommon thing. They've formed a community corporation—open to more than 1,000 producing, refining, and distributing organizations. . . . Into this united enterprise the industry is taking as partner a Fourth Musketeer—the Public—whose interest is paramount in everything oil means to the people of the world and the society in which they live."

I must apologize for my tardiness at this rendezvous; my yellow horse cast a shoe en route and I fell in with a breathlessly beautiful creature named Milady de Winter whose honor I am prepared to disparage at the drop of a hat. However, now that all the board members are here, I'd like to make a few restrictions about the way the firm is going to be run in the future. And much as I hate to get tough, gentlemen, this is twenty-five per cent of the voting stock talking.

First of all, our station attendants—those young men with the teeth. What business are we in, selling gas or bridgework? That five hundred miles from Los Angeles to San Francisco isn't a highway, it's a dental display. According to this memo from our Mr. Fruhauf, we are employing thousands of boys with matchless profiles and teeth like pearls to stand around and remind the customers they need porcelain inlays more than lubrication. Let's face it—the public is sick of clean-limbed youths in spotless white drill. I move we junk this personnel and replace it with an older type of man. We have been offered a very attractive deal by a factor in Atlanta who will deliver a practically toothless style of attendant, on the order of Jeeter Lester, with snuff on his lapel and guaranteed absolutely free from *esprit de corps*, whom we can pay off in turnips. These men, by the way, are fine old American stock and hail from the pine scrub where there are very few unions, so I don't feel there would be any compromise with our past traditions. And while we're on it, let's junk Fruhauf. I was watching him out there at the water cooler a minute ago, and anybody who uses three Lily cups at a clip is not a well man.

Next, what about the stations themselves, the "lubritoriums" I believe you call them? What kind of an impression does it make on the consumer when a man in khaki overalls comes out of a Williamsburgh restoration and says "Gas 'er up?" You can't do this Colonial thing by halves; let's either dress the help in tricornes, powdered wigs, and knee breeches, or switch to some other period. As a matter of fact, I think the public would snap up a Tobacco Road filling station, for instance—a fall-down shanty with a leaky roof, some rusty jalopies, and a couple of mental defectives scratching themselves in the yard. I'm sure my factor in Atlanta could supply the latter items if we gave him enough time—say, half an hour. Or we might possibly go in for a touch of elegance: raspberry ceilings and Beidermeier, attendants in white tie, delicious little canapés, and a free Lonsdale epigram with every grease job. In such a setup the defectives wouldn't be wasted and I doubt whether they'd even be noticed.

Finally, there is this matter of service. We have made such a fetish of service that before the driver shuts off the ignition, our attendants are swarming up his car like powder monkeys, polishing the headlights, replenishing the water and giving him everything short of a free tonsillectomy. This only frightens him and makes him conscious he's in a hurry. There is no reason why the service man cannot surreptitiously abstract one of those pins from the engine and spend a pleasant hour or two tinkering and chatting. A handful of some gentle abrasive like emery dust, secreted in the suede cloth used to polish the windshield, often points up the necessity of good vision, and in turn makes the register tinkle gaily. There are many similar devices for promoting leisurely contacts and swelling monthly sales, without resorting to stabbing and rolling the customer.

That just about winds up the agenda as far as I'm concerned, and if one of you boys can provide me with a fresh mount, I'll change my ping to purr and clatter along to Dijon. I'm supposed to engage ten varlets in sword-play on the steps of the Cardinal's palace, and here it is four o'clock already. Hold my stirrup, will you, somebody? Well, happy motoring!

If an In-law Meet an Outlaw

I WAS STRETCHED OUT soaking blissfully in the tub this morning—well, not actually stretched out; more crouched in an old wash boiler with the janitor turning a watering can over me—when I was suddenly suffused with a sense of the utmost well-being, as though someone had just presented me with a billion tax-free dollars. I sprang out of the boiler, wrapped myself in a fleecy Circassian girl who happened to be hanging there, and leafed rapidly through my mail. Outside of a terse note from the public library reporting that my request for a card had been approved, and three swatches of tweed from a Hollywood tailor, there seemed to be no grounds for elation. On thc contrary, the mound of bills and summonses clearly indicated the bailiffs were on my tail and determined to clap me into Marshalsea Prison for debt. After scratching about a while, however, I managed to reconstruct my train of thought. It was simple enough. It had merely occurred to me that though my youth is rapidly receding into the distance, old age has one sweet consolation in store. There are going to be fewer and fewer of those family get-togethers over the holidays.

Why anybody in his right mind doesn't hop into bed like Turkey Gehrke the day before Thanksgiving and stay there until the relatives clear is beyond me. From Halloween to the Ides of March, the average American home is constantly filled with a succession of heavy, overfed uncles dozing on lounges, their uneasy slumber punctuated now and again by a voluptuous belch. The next time you take the only girl in the world in your arms and look into those violet pools, remember one thing. You're simply a peg on which she hopes to hang a series of family dinners. You may think you're Galahad, or Monsieur Beaucaire, or Henry Kaiser, but you're not. You're only a caterer.

Where the relatives come from, once the banns are posted, from under what stones, it is impossible to say. Personally, I jilted hundreds of deucedly attractive girls solely because of their folks. In my search for a helpmeet, I interviewed scores of applicants from every clime: buxom, taffy-haired wenches from Copenhagen, sloe-eyed Eurasians from the Bubbling Well Road, saucy midinettes from the Rue de Rivoli, cool Devonshire beauties with skin like clotted cream, and placid, deep-bosomed wildflowers from the Kirghiz Steppe. In every case the candidate had family somewhere in the background, crouched ready to make my life a hell. At length I met a tall and lovely dryad from the Lone Star State, imperious yet tender, innocent but incredibly versed in womanly wiles. Damn my eyes, sir, she was as pretty as a peony. I loved her for herself alone, but I took the precaution of looking her up in Dun and Bradstreet. Her people had left her four hundred thousand acres in the Panhandle, a controlling interest in United States Steel, and a twin-Diesel yacht sleeping twelve. Every hour, on the hour, three men ran in with bushel baskets and emptied a flood of gold eagles around her feet. She swore she had no kin; I had lawyers trace her lineage back to Frederick Barbarossa until they confirmed it. The day of our wedding dawned on schedule. As we mounted the steps of St. Thomas', her eyes streaming with gratitude at having won such a prize, a gnarled old desert rat touched his forelock. She acknowledged the greeting absently.

"Who's that?" I demanded, recoiling.

"My uncle," she replied. "He's a sheepherder from Canberra. He's coming to dinner tomorrow night." I bent over on the pretext of tying my bootlace, squirmed adroitly through a policeman's legs, and in forty-eight hours was paddling up the St. Lawrence under an assumed name.

For all my vigilance, nevertheless, retribution overtook me at last. When I finally struck the colors to the breathtaking creature who shares my joint account, I was satisfied she was an orphan. Her one living tie was a rheumatic King Charles spaniel, and even then I persuaded it to sign a paper releasing me from any obligation. At my insistence, we were married in the dead of night on an islet off Casco Bay; I instantly cut down the parson and witnesses, left a cairn to mark their lonely grave, and headed back to the mainland. Only the stars knew our secret, I exulted to myself.

And then, within the week, her relatives started filing forward. Puling babes and graybeard loons sprang from our carpet as from a seedbed. Jail doors yawned to disgorge maternal uncles; elderly harpies in bombazine, bearing patience plants, trooped through the bathroom deriding our linens. Pimply nephews awoke me at eight in the morning to put the sleeve on me for a small loan.

The average man would have lost his head, screamed and threatened divorce; not so I. I gently took my wife's windpipe between the forefinger and thumb of the left hand and massaged it until she agreed that no relative would ever again cross the threshold. The device worked for a while, but gradually she undermined me. More and more faces began appearing at the holiday board; today it looks like the Congress of Vienna. Every Christmas I pay off on a hundred and thirty-two turkeys and all I ever get is a drumstick. That's wedlock, brother.

Last Thanksgiving, for instance, I was curled up peacefully like a shrimp, mouth ajar and halfway through a thrilling dream in which Jane Russell had stopped at my mountain lodge to dry her things. Just as she had retired behind the screen and I was purling, "Why, little girl, I'm old enough to be your father," the doorbell wrenched me from my fantasy. I landed convulsively on the bedroom floor, flailing at the air. The *signora* finished applying make-up to lips already like coral, and rose from her dressing table.

"Welcome back, sweet," she snapped. "Dust a bit of talc on that beard and greet our guests. They've been here over an hour."

As I scrambled into my clothes, I could hear the jackals in the living room opening my last bottle of liqueur Scotch and discussing me freely.

"He'll never amount to a damn," stated a brother-in-law who had quit work during the Harding Administration. "It's the kids I'm sorry for."

"Did you see that mark under her eye?" whispered a niece. "He threw a cottage pudding at her in a fit of temper."

"I met him coming out of a pawnshop Tuesday," related another. "He had his arm around a platinum blonde."

They had finished the Scotch and were opening the cooking sherry when I entered. The premises were filled with steam and a sickening smell of giblets. Besides the usual covetous faces, there were several unfamiliar ones—a merchant sailor who mistakenly supposed himself at a radio broadcast and an aged beldame with an ear trumpet who kept asking querulously for the next train to Cynwyd.

Over the hubbub, from the kitchen, floated madame's voice offering to triple the maid's salary if she would stay through dinner. Selecting one of the less revolting young cousins, I sat down by him and attempted to draw him into conversation.

"Well, what kept you out of the army, Mac?" I inquired genially. "You're a big strong hulk."

With a boorishness typical of the entire clan, he stalked off, obviously flustered by my question. By now, the company had divided roughly into two groups—the older matrons dissecting my wife's clothes and their menfolk predicting my impending bankruptcy. At three o'clock, when the dinner bell sounded, the room was revolving about me like a carousel. By the time I fought my way to the table, the turkey had dwindled to a pathetic little pile of bones. I tamped down a glutinous amalgam of sweet potatoes and marshmallows, and retired to the drawing room to chink up the crannies with English walnuts. The room was empty, save for a nephew sprawled on the floor tearing random pages out of my first editions and a stray grandfather with snuff on his lapel.

"Hello, sonny," he quavered. "Who be you—friend of the family?" I grunted noncommittally and tried extracting what nourishment I could from a strip of preserved orange peel. The old gaffer peered furtively over his shoulder, leaned closer to me. "You look like a nice, clean-cut young feller," he observed, "so I'll give you some advice. Don't never sign a note for the bozo that lives here."

"I happen to be the bozo," I snarled, rising with awful majesty.

"Yes, I know," he said hurriedly, "but I'm just warnin' you. He's a crook; he'd steal your eyeteeth. Any time you see a man with them little pig eyes——" I burst my bonds spang in the middle of my character analysis and finished the evening under a table in a neighborhood tavern. It was drafty and I got sawdust in my ears, but at least the cat I met there had no grudge against me. He wasn't even a second cousin by marriage.

Take Two Parts Sand, One Part Girl, and Stir

OUTSIDE OF THE THREE R'S—the razor, the rope, and the revolver—I know only one sure-fire method of coping with the simmering heat we may cheerfully expect in this meridian from now to Labor Day. Whenever the mercury starts inching up the column, I take to the horizontal plane with a glass graduate trimmed with ferns, place a pinch of digitalis or any good heart stimulant at my elbow, and flip open the advertising section of *Vogue*. Fifteen minutes of that paradisiacal prose, those dizzying non sequiturs, and my lips are as blue as Lake Louise. If you want a mackerel iced or a sherbet frozen, just bring it up and let me read the advertising section of *Vogue* over it. I can also take care of small picnic parties up to five. The next time you're hot and breathless, remember the name, folks: Little Labrador Chilling & Dismaying Corporation.

It would require precision instruments as yet undreamed of to decide whether *Vogue*'s advertisements contain more moonbeams per linear inch than those of its competitors, but the June issue was certainly a serious contender for the ecstasy sweepstakes. There was, for instance, the vagary which portrayed a Revolutionary heroine setting fire to a field of grain with this caption: "*The Patriotism in Her Heart Burned Wheat Fields.* It took courage that day in October 1777 for Catherine Schuyler to apply the torch to her husband's wheat fields so that food would not fall into the hands of the enemy. The flames that consumed the wheat fields on the Schuyler estate near Saratoga burned with no greater brightness than the patriotism in Catherine Schuyler's heart." Then, with a triple forward somersault that would have done credit to Alfredo Codona, the wizard of the trapeze, the copywriter vaulted giddily into an appeal to American women to augment their loveliness with Avon Cosmetics. Somewhat breathless, I turned the page and beheld a handsome young air woman crouched on a wing of her plane. "Test Pilot—Size 10," read the text. "Nine thousand feet above the flying field, a Hellcat fighter plane screams down in the dark blur of a power dive. Holding the stick of this four-hundred-mile-an-hour ship is a small firm hand." The owner of the small firm hand, I shortly discovered in the verbal power dive that followed, is an enthusiastic patron of DuBarry Beauty Preparations. The transition in logic was so abrupt that it was only by opening my mouth and screaming briefly, a procedure I had observed in the movies, that I was able to keep my eardrums from bursting.

The most singular display of the advertiser's eternal lust for novelty, though, was a bold, full-color photograph of an olive-skinned beauty, buried up to her corsage in sand, in the interests of Marvella Simulated Pearls. A matched string of the foregoing circled her voluptuous throat, and dimly visible in the background were a conch shell and a sponge, identifying the locale as the seaside. The model's face exhibited a resentment verging on ferocity, which was eminently pardonable; anybody mired in a quicksand, with only a string of simulated pearls to show for it, has a justifiable beef. And so have I. The connection between burning wheat field and cosmetic jar, Hellcat fighter and lipstick, is tenuous enough, God knows, but somehow the copyrighter managed to link them with his sophistries. Why in Tophet a scowling nude stuck bolt upright in a sand bar should influence the reader to rush to his jeweller for a particular brand of artificial pearl, however, I cannot possibly imagine.

Perhaps if we reconstruct the circumstances under which this baffling campaign was conceived, a clue might be forthcoming. Let us, therefore, don a clean collar and sidle discreetly into the offices of Meeker, Cassavant, Singleton, Doubleday & Tripler, a fairly representative advertising agency.

[*Scene: The Brain Room of the agency, a conference chamber decorated in cerebral gray, Swedish modern furniture, and the inevitable Van Gogh reproductions. As the curtain rises, Duckworth, the copy chief, and four members of his staff—Farish, Munkaczi, DeGroot, and Miss Drehdel—are revealed plunged in thought.*]

DUCKWORTH (*impatiently*): Well, what do you say, Farish? Got an angle, DeGroot?

FARISH: I still keep going back to my old idea, V. J.

DUCKWORTH: What's that?

FARISH (*thirstily*): A good red-hot picture of a dame in a transparent shimmy, with plenty of thems and those (*suddenly conscious of Miss Drehdel's presence*)—oh, excuse me.

MISS DREHDEL (*wearily*): That's all right. I read Earl Wilson's column, too.

FARISH: And a balloon coming out of her mouth saying, "I've had my Vita-Ray Cheese Straws today—*have you?*"

DUCKWORTH: No-o-o, it doesn't—it doesn't *sing*, if you know what I mean. I feel there's something gay and youthful and alive about these cheese straws. That's the note I want to hear in our copy.

DEGROOT: How about a gay, newborn baby in a crib? That would include the various elements. I'd like to see a line like "No harsh abrasives to upset tender tummies."

DUCKWORTH: No, it's static. To me it lacks dynamism.

MISS DREHDEL: What's wrong with a closeup of the cheese straws and "20 cents a box" underneath?

DUCKWORTH: Oversimplification. They'd never get it.

MUNKACZI (*violently*): I've got it, V. J., *I've got it!*

DUCKWORTH: What?

MUNKACZI: We'll take one of these Conover models and bury her up to her neck in sand! Maybe some driftwood or a couple of clams for drama!

FARISH: How do we tie in the cheese straws?

MUNKACZI: I haven't worked it out yet, but it smells right to me.

DUCKWORTH (*excitedly*): Wait a minute, now—you threw me into something when you said "sand." What we need is grit—punch—conflict. I see a foxhole at Anzio—shells bursting—a doughboy with shining eyes saying, "This is what I'm fighting for, Ma—freedom of purchase the American Way—the right to buy Vita-Ray Cheese Straws on every drug, grocery, and delicatessen counter from coast to coast!"

FARISH: Man, oh man, that's terrific! I'll buy that!

DEGROOT: It's poetic and yet it's timely, too! It's a blockbuster, V. J.!

DUCKWORTH (*radiant*): You really mean it? You're sure you're not telling me this just because I'm the boss? (*Indignation in varying degree from all*) O.K. If there's one thing I can't abide, it's a lot of yes men around me. Now let's get on to the Hush-a-Bye Blanket account. Any hunches?

DEGROOT: We got a darb. (*Producing two photographs*) This is what the nap of a Hush-a-Bye looks like under the microscope.

FARISH: And here's the average blanket. See the difference?

DUCKWORTH: Why, yes. It has twice as many woollen fibers as the Hush-a-Bye.

DEGROOT (*happily*): Check. There's our campaign.

DUCKWORTH: Hmm. Isn't that sort of defeatist?

FARISH: A little, but it shows we don't make extravagant claims.

DEGROOT: We could always switch the photographs.

FARISH: Sure, nobody ever looks at their blanket through a microscope.

DUCKWORTH (*dubiously*): We-e-ll, I don't know. I like your approach to the challenge, but I don't think you've extracted its—its thematic milk, shall I say. Now, I for one saw a different line of attack.

FARISH (*instantly*): Me too, V. J. What I visualize is a showgirl with a real nifty chassis in a peekaboo night gown. Here, I'll draw you a sketch—

MISS DREHDEL: Don't bother. We can read your mind.

MUNKACZI: Listen, V. J., do you want a wrinkle that'll revolutionize the business? Answer yes or no.

DUCKWORTH: Does it fit in with the product?

MUNKACZI: Fit in? It grows right out of it! You're looking at a beach, see? Voom! Right in front of you is a Powers girl buried up to the bust in sand, with some horseshoe crabs or seaweed as an accent.

DUCKWORTH: Do you see a Hush-a-Bye blanket anywhere in the composition?

MUNKACZI: No, that would be hitting it on the nose. Indirection, V. J., that's the whole trend today.

DUCKWORTH: You've realized the problem, Munkaczi, but your synthesis is faulty. I miss a sense of scope. Who are we rooting for?

MUNKACZI: Well, of course I was only spitballing. I haven't had time to explore every cranny.

DUCKWORTH: Look, kids, if you don't like what I'm about to suggest, will you tell me?

FARISH (*fiercely*): I've never been a stooge for anyone yet.

DEGROOT: You said it. There's not enough money in the world to buy *my* vote.

DUCKWORTH: That's the stuff. I want guts in this organization, not a bunch of namby-pambies scared that I'll kick 'em out into the breadline. Now this is hazy, mind you, but it's all there. A beachhead in the Solomons—a plain, ordinary G.I. Joe in a slit trench, grinning at the consumer through the muck and grime on his face, and asking, "Are you backing me up with Hush-a-Bye Blankets at home? Gee, Mom, don't sabotage my birthright with sleazy, inferior brands!"

DEGROOT: Holy cow, that'll tear their hearts out!

FARISH (*with a sob*): It brings a lump to your throat. It's a portion of common everyday experience.

DUCKWORTH: Remember, men, it isn't sacred. If you think you can improve the phrasing—

DEGROOT: I wouldn't change a word of it.

FARISH: It's got balance and flow and discipline. Say it again, will you, V. J.?

DUCKWORTH: No, it's pretty near lunch and we still need a slant for the Marvella Pearl people.

MUNKACZI (*exalted*): Your troubles are over, boss. I got something that leaps from the printed page into the hearts of a million women! It's four A.M. in the Aleutians. A haggard, unshaven Marine is kneeling in a shell hole, pointing his rifle at you and whispering, "Start thinking, sister! When Johnny comes marching home are you going to be poised and serene with Marvella Pearls or just another housewife?"

FARISH: Cripes, I had the same notion, V. J. He took the words right out of my mouth!

DEGROOT: I'll go for that! It's as timely as tomorrow's newspaper!

DUCKWORTH: There's only one thing wrong with it. It's *too* timely.

DEGROOT (*eagerly*): That's what I meant. It's depressing.

FARISH: It reminds people of their troubles. Ugh!

DUCKWORTH: Precisely. Now, I've been mulling a concept which is a trifle on the exotic side but fundamentally sound. Mark you, I'm merely talking out loud. A girl on a bathing beach, almost totally buried in the sand, with a Marvella necklace and a brooding, inscrutable expression like the

Sphinx. Haunting but inviting—the eternal riddle of womankind.

DeGroot (*emotionally*): V. J., do you want my candid opinion? I wouldn't tell this to my own mother, but you've just made advertising history!

Farish: It's provocative, muscular, three-dimensional! It's got a *spiral* quality, the more you think of it.

Duckworth: How does it hit you, Munkaczi?

Munkaczi (*warmly*): I couldn't like it more if it was my own idea.

Duckworth: I wonder if Miss Drehdel can give us the woman's reaction, in a word.

Miss Drehdel (*rising*): You bet I can. The word I'm thinking of rhymes with Sphinx. (*Sunnily*) Well, good-by now. If anybody wants me, I'm over at Tim's, up to here in sawdust and Cuba Libres. (*She goes; a pause.*)

Farish: I always said there was something sneaky about her.

DeGroot: Women and business don't mix.

Munkaczi: You can never tell what they're really thinking.

Farish (*cackling*): Old V. J. smoked her out though, didn't he?

Duckworth (*expansively*): Yes, I may be wrong, but this is one conference she won't forget in a hurry, eh, boys? (*As the boys chuckle loyally and scuffle to light his cigar.*)

CURTAIN

Caution—Soft Prose Ahead

I DON'T want to shame anybody, but while you lazy slugs were lying abed this morning, all knotted up in the sheets and covered with a fine perspiration, Mummy had been up for hours in her gardening apron and floppy hat, shearing great, showy blooms from the publishers' fall announcements. Whether it was that rainy spell or what, there has never been a year like this for the giant double-flowering fatuity and gorgeous variegated drivel. Is there anything you can catch from being around too much overripe beauty? I feel a little faint.

It may seem arbitrary to select for one's affection any single title from twenty catalogues full of them, yet there is something so artless, so downright dewy, about G. P. Putnam's Sons issuing a book called *Trout Fishing in New Zealand in War Time* that you want to rush up to their editorial offices, tuck back their beards, and smother them with kisses. It's a pity that so sweeping a title, embracing, as it does, sport, travel, and war, couldn't have sneaked in a romantic complication as well, like *Trout Fishing with Lana Turner in New Zealand in War Time.* Second to Putnam's in my love parade are Farrar & Rinehart with *Sniffy: The Story of a Skunk,* by David M. Stearns, who is also author of *Chuckle: The Story of a Woodchuck.* If Mr. Stearns ever does a book on labor, he could do worse than call it *Finkle: The Story of a Fink.* Another rippling title promised for late this month by the John Day Company is *Piskey Folk,* by Enys Tregarthen. *Piskey Folk* is a book of Cornish legends, the nature of which is extremely vague even to the John Day Company:

> Not all the legends published here are of the Piskeys. The seagoing little people of "Bucca Boo's Little Merry Men" and the gnomes of "The Gnome Maiden" play their parts as well; and "A Brotherhood of Little Shadows" presents no little people at all, but a cast of even more nebulous characters in a tale which for beauty of imagery is perhaps unrivalled in folklore.

Frankly, I got so confused by this dreamy précis that I had to loosen my tiny stays and pour myself a wee dram before I could continue.

To imply that the John Day list is the only one touched with moon magic, however, would be grossly unfair. Henry Holt & Co. are patting their back hair rather self-consciously over a new book called *Skittles,* by Rosemary Lamkey. Just what Miss Lamkey's book is about is hard to say, but here is the plotkey:

> Skittles, the hero of this story, is fond of wool-gathering, even though he knows it is wrong. And when he is caught barehanded, he lies. He does that so well, he believes his lies himself! That works until, intent upon some specially lovely wool, he falls *plop!* into a bog, and can't get out. When rescuers ask how he got there, he can't tell the real reason, and each time he lies, he sinks deeper, and his rescuers can't get him out. So they leave him, and after a long time Skittles finally admits the truth to himself, and then the bog releases him. After that, Skittles knows how to tell the difference between the truth and a lie. One of Skittles' friends is a bee, Blzz, and he lives with his mother in a beautiful fairy cottage, and his friends and his house and his rescuers all appear in full colors on the pages of this handsome book.

Maybe it was the sound of the bee's name that got me, but at this juncture a small cloud appeared over my hammock, inside it a log of wood with a saw going through it and the caption "Z-z-z." Had it not been for two comical tramps named Weary Willie and Dusty Rhodes, who stopped by to beg some pie and milk, I should have been sleeping yet.

Probably the most sullen title of the year is that of a shopping guide by Kay Austin, announced by Carrick & Evans: *What Do You Want for $1.98?* I cannot feel that this is the best of all possible titles for a book intended to retail for exactly one dollar and ninety-eight cents, no matter how apropos its subject matter. The average reader, in the first flush of resentment, is liable to turn a dusty pink and pitch the book into the fire before he catches on to the pun (or whatever it is). Of course, the book could be printed on asbestos, but the expense would put it beyond the reach of most readers. Or is that what I had in mind in the first place?

No publishing season passes without its complement of novelty books, but this year such mandarins as Frederick A. Stokes and Appleton-Century have flung discretion to the winds and are kicking up their heels like colts in a pasture. The former is sponsoring something rather spicy called *Fun with Sting*, by Leeming, while the latter's *Betcha Can't Do It*, by Alexander van Rensselaer, is a cinch for the curiosa trade, explaining "how to put twelve persons in eleven beds and numerous other intriguing stunts which will break the ice at any party." Apparently the feeling around Appleton-Century is that now is the time for the Piskey folk to come to the aid of the party, for among other piquant icebreakers in this manual will be found directions on "how to crawl under a broom" and "how to put your head through a calling card." If the publishers would like to include an old Creole recipe, which has been in my family for generations, on "how to go soak your head in a bottle of milk," I shall be only too pleased to send it on.

In the field of humor, Frederick A. Stokes is grooming a veritable pippin in the form of a high-spirited travesty on *How to Read a Book,* by Mortimer J. Adler. It is called *How to Read Two Books,* by Erasmus G. Addlepate (get it?), and is obviously the work of Joe, the stockroom boy. I see Joe as a rather big boy of fifteen whose literary output to date consists of an unproduced play about the bridge craze called *The Glorious Fourth* and a hilarious parody of *Gone with the Wind* called *Come with the Breeze.* The most the Stokes catalogue will admit to booksellers is this:

> We have been repeatedly foiled in our numerous attempts to discover the identity of the famous author, lecturer, numismatist, and entrepreneur who lurks behind the pseudonym of Erasmus G. Addlepate.

[How about it? Is that Joe, the stockroom boy, or not?]

> If Mr. Addlepate's skill at lurking exceeds *our* skill at detection, you might just as well not bother *your* pretty head about it, but just go ahead and sell *How to Read Two Books.*

All right, fellows, that's a deal. Not only won't we bother our pretty heads about it but we'll go further: the next one who ever mentions the subject of publishing or publishers is a rotten egg. That is, all except my dream boys, G. P. Putnam's Sons, who, in their description of Isabel Paterson's novel *If It Prove Fair Weather,* indulge in one last magnificent orgy of self-analysis. "The new novel," says the blurb, "concerns Emily Cruger, who loves her man and can't get him. The man is James Nathaniel Wishart, a stuffed shirt who is also a publisher, a maddening sort of man who nevertheless comes to fascinate Emily as well as to drive her nearly insane with rage and laughter."

Move over, Emily.

Hit Him Again, He's Sober

HAD THE LATE Henry James been standing on the steps of his house at 21 Washington Place early this morning, he would have seen the deponent, his neighbor, totter out of a cab and collapse with a sob in the arms of the night elevator man. No doubt Mr. James, who oddly enough *was* standing there gassing with Mark Twain and Richard Harding Davis, imagined he was seeing just another drunk. That is Mr. James's privilege; personally, I do not give a fig for his good opinion of me. But I do most definitely want to clarify the incident before it becomes distorted. It is typical of our sick civilization that a man as temperate as myself, abstemious to the point of fanaticism, should become the butt of gossip. And yet, paradoxically, it was my very sobriety that brought down on me vilification and physical abuse worse than was ever heaped on an early Christian martyr.

The whole wretched affair began yesterday afternoon. When the late sunlight filtered through the blinds onto my Tyrian-purple couch, it revealed a very sick man. Three Lilliputians in doublet and hose, armed with nutpicks and oyster forks, were enfilading my big toe, from which the letters "O-U-C-H" zigzagged away into infinity. During the night, parties unknown had removed my corneas, varnished and replaced them, and fitted me with a curious steel helmet, several sizes too small. Lying there cradled between softest Fruit of the Loom, a deep cocoa-flavored sense of remorse welled upward from the knees and constricted my heart.

"You mucker," I said through my teeth, "if you've an ounce of manhood in your make-up, you'll get down on all fours and beg her forgiveness." This gaudy monologue continued uninterrupted through my ablutions, except when the can of tooth powder slipped from my fingers and exploded on the floor with a roar like a fragmentation bomb. A few seconds later, I entered my wife's presence with the smug exaltation of a character out of a Hall Caine novel, clothed in a white dimity frock and a blue hair ribbon, fingering the temperance badge pinned to my breast.

"I'm through," I declaimed. "Never again. Good-by, John

Barleycorn, hello, Walker-Gordon. *Mens sana in corpore sano.* Look at this hand—steady as a rock." My peach blossom looked up from her buhl writing cabinet, shrugged coldly, and resumed adding up the liquor bill. Determined to prove I had undergone a moral regeneration worthy of *Pilgrim's Progress,* I conjured up a corn popper and a volume of Colley Cibber's memoirs and snuggled down before the hearth. After I had read in silence for twenty seconds, the pica type tired my eyes and I leaned my head on my hand for support. Suddenly the phone shrilled and I arose, adroitly demolishing a vase of chrysanthemums. Two members of our young married set were holding an impromptu cocktail party. Next to Mrs. George Washington Kavanaugh, they assured me, my presence would establish it as the social event of the season. I was refusing politely but firmly when I heard my wife whinny over my shoulder.

"A party! A party!" she bleated. "You never take me to a party! I want to go to the party! Party . . . party . . . party . . ." Before I could reason with her, she flung herself on the counterpane and started sobbing into the bolster. Aware of the futility of trying to combat tears with logic, I acceded wearily. On the way uptown in the taxi, however, I made it plain that my decision to abstain from alcohol was irrevocable. My wife's lip curled superciliously. "Tell it to Sweeney," she advised. I leaned over to Sweeney, who was beating an impatient tattoo on the steering wheel while waiting for the lights to change, and told him my decision to abstain was irrevocable. His contemptuous chuckle infuriated me, and I lost my head. "You wait, the two of you!" I screamed, hammering my tiny fists on the jump seat. "May I fall down dead if I so much as touch a drop!" I was still defying the lightning as we swept into the pleasure pavilion. Eighteen or twenty voluptuaries, in varying stages of repair, were holding wassail in a cozy two-room apartment. To make the proceedings more intimate, someone had introduced a Great Dane, a parakeet, and a progressive child who was busily emptying fruit rinds and cigarette ends into the men's hats. Yet amid the sickening debauch, suggesting Babylon at its most dissolute (Babylon, Long Island, that is), I stood a figure apart, a pillar unmoved by the blandishments and mockery of my fellows.

"Just one teentsy-weentsy sip," begged my hostess, a tantalizing blonde, all black georgette and open-mesh stockings. "Don't be thataway, you inflexible boy." For a moment her dear nearness maddened me, but I resolutely averted my face and called for a glass of Adam's ale. The more turbulent the carousal, the more steadfast I became; Cromwell at his flintiest was an orchid compared to me. In my foolish pride, I believed that I had found the philosopher's stone, that I was immune from disaster. And then the Moving Finger moved. The host, a broth of a boy who had once run seventy-nine yards down the Bowl with the Harvard backfield clinging to his waist, linked arms with me.

"Going get you sandwich," he proposed indistinctly.

"Come on kitchen." I rashly extricated myself and stepped away. As I did, he reached down to the vicinity of his tibia and came up with a haymaker that caught me flush on the button. An interesting display of Catherine wheels, Very lights, and star shells flashed before me, and uttering a taut "Mamma," I melted into the parquet. I awoke on a pile of krimmer coats in the bedroom to discover my wife applying a cold poultice to the submaxillary region. In between embrocations, the Angel of the Crimea, her cheeks aflame with Martinis, informed me that I had forever alienated us from the beau monde. I had deliberately pinched the hostess, kicked two Whitneys in the shin, and smashed a priceless collection of Royal Worcester china. I protested I was innocent, a victim of some hideous conspiracy. "I'm as sober as you are!" I pleaded. "Soberer! I haven't had a dram since yesterday!" "Yes, yes," she agreed soothingly. "Help me with him, will you, Ariadne? His legs get rubbery at this stage." Before I could wrench free, kind hands thrust me into a topcoat, jammed an alien derby over my ears in the classic manner of Ben Welch, and hustled me downstairs in a freight elevator. While I kept trying to raise my head, which hung dahlia-like on its stalk, the rescuers started wrangling over my future.

"Take him home. . . . No, he'll cut himself. . . . Who is he? . . . I know a spot where we can get him some soup. . . . Yeah, soup's good." I gurgled a feeble remonstrance that passed unnoticed; when the dust blew away, I was propped up at a table in a sleazy bar off the Gay White Way, staring wanly into a bowl of buttermilk. My wife and her grouping had disappeared and a noisy Syrian, representing himself as the owner of a chain of shoe stores in Hartford, was offering to take me into partnership. Midway in his harangue, he broke off and, hailing the bartender as "Four Eyes," ordered him to serve me a highball. The gibe evidently climaxed a long, hard day for the bartender. With a hoarse bellow, he hurdled the beerpulls and uncorked a left hook that I intercepted nimbly with my ear. The Syrian thereupon lashed out handily and in a moment I was bobbing between them like a cork. The estimate is, of course, unofficial, but sports writers have since estimated that I stopped more punches than Jacob "Soldier" Bartfield in his entire career.

I came to in an alley with two handsome shiners suitable for framing and the Hall Johnson Choir singing "Stabat Mater" inside my head. My wife had mysteriously reappeared and, aided by a shrill young couple, whose dialogue had been written for them by Clyde Fitch, was sponging me off. "Now take it easy, will you?" she implored, brushing back my widow's peak. "Everything is going to be all right. Just relax." I closed my eyes with a grateful sigh. When I opened them again, I was lying on a banquette in a clip joint off Amsterdam Avenue. Dawn was peeping in at the window and a spurious gypsy violinist was rendering gems from *The Bohemian Girl*. At the next table, a gaunt trio resembling Picasso's "The Absinthe Drinker," dimly identifiable as my wife and the Fitches, was sobbing brokenly for Alt Wien. I stumbled to my feet, flung my last bit of collateral at the management, and, herding the revellers before me, started toward the door. Right outside it stood two monumental Texans fourteen feet high, with snow on their hair, clamoring for admission. The ensuing action is somewhat hazy, but as I reconstruct it, our Mr. Fitch curtly bade Gog and Magog step aside, employing the informal phrase "you big crackers." I was scudding across the sidewalk, primly keeping my nose clean and my lips buttoned, when I abruptly felt myself seized by the collar and hoisted four feet into the air.

"What did you call me, you little measle?" one of the ogres was rumbling. "Why, I'll flatten that bugle—" He drew back a fist no larger than a peanut-fed ham; the breeze from the gesture alone dizzied me. I croaked out a pitiable denial and he let me drop. The fall nearly broke my ankles. In that instant, as I slunk after my party, I reached the most vital decision of my life. Three times in one evening I had pursed my lips against the grape and thrice my life had hung in the balance. Come hell or high water, famine, flood, or fire, I was through with milk and large moral resolutions. From here in, it's high carnival and strange purple sins. Bring me another pair of those amber witches, waiter, and go easy on the club soda.

Ye Olde Ivory Tower

Is THERE ANYBODY around here who is looking for a nice personal chest fox? If there is, he need go no further. I am a fifty-one-year-old Spartan boy and I am interested in finding a good home for my pet. There just doesn't seem to be room enough for both of us inside this tunic.

I first detected the gnawing sensation one morning several months ago while opening my mail. I don't want to go off the deep end, but if there is a mailing list west of the Great Smokies which doesn't carry my name, I am prepared to eat its mimeograph stencils. My museum of Harris-tweed swatches has, I flatter myself, achieved a certain small renown, and I am currently preparing a definitive monograph on the twenty-seven varieties of French hand laundries. But if ever a letter resisted classification, even under the Miscellaneous and/or Screwball Division, it was Mr. Harry Oliver's.

Mr. Oliver, for twenty-one years a Hollywood art director, has decided that what writers need most at this particular point is an authentic reproduction of an Early American village "to serve as the ideal hideaway, workplace, or recreation spot." I don't know what it is writers would want to hide away from, except mimeographed letters from art directors, but those were his words. "Would you approve," he continued, "of an Early American pioneer village, a quaint, interesting old Inn with its old-time taproom, wholesome Early American dwellings of real cedar logs, split shakes, hewn timbers, honest stone fireplaces [as distinguished, I presume, from dishonest stone fireplaces], and chimneys?" To one who had been struggling along with plain old-fashioned shakes, it came as a painful surprise that Mr. Oliver proposed splitting them. But he was quick to anticipate any possible objections. "Bear in mind, of course," he warned, "that pure Early American comfort, the old rocking chair, big fireplaces, even the old feather bed, all would be combined with every convenience of the modern age." To clarify opinion on his settlement, Mr. Oliver enclosed a questionnaire with some of the most tantalizing queries imaginable. "Can writers get along with writers?" asked this gentleman who had spent twenty-one years in Hollywood, following this up with the even more surprising question, "Does it matter?" A request for "Your name for the village" was, of course, too enticing to pass over. Pencilling in "Reason Totters," which seemed to me to give the whole enterprise a fine old English flavor, I tore the questionnaire into four neat strips, filed them away in a basket I reserve for the purpose, and crept back to my old feather bed to think Early American thoughts about Mr. Oliver.

I had lain doggo for about a week when another letter came winging in, containing a cross-section of comment on the project by a number of writers. Leo A. Smith, editor of the Oxnard, California *Evening Press*, announced with what could be either enthusiasm or profound fatigue, "It will be a good hideout for a gang more or less alike." Walt Keene, disdainful of rhetoric, observed with majestic simplicity, "It is my Castle in Spain." Irvin Willat took the view that the colony "should have a hall for community entertainment," conjuring up a vision of grizzled scenarists in buckskin drinking forty-rod and dancing an old-fashioned hoedown. Jerry Cady of Hollywood, on the other hand, spoke out vigorously for a streamlined Walden: "It should have a research library and stenographic service." Sig Herzig, also of Hollywood, beat me to the punch by keynoting, "I'm starting to relax already." I finished Mr. Oliver's letter in such an advanced state of relaxation that blankets and hot coffee were necessary before my pulse was heard to flicker. When at last I had weathered the crisis, our gruff old family physician took my trembling, blue-veined checkbook in his hand and wrung a promise from me that I would open only one in every four letters.

At distant intervals thereafter fugitive postcards arrived from Mr. Oliver, their messages charged with a warm, almost steamy intimacy. He invariably addressed me as "Writer Folks: Just to let you know that everything is going along fine-and-dandy with our Writers' Colony. You might be interested to know that a great many folks plan to build first a small log cabin, to be used in the future as a guest house, or a workplace away from the rest of the household." A site had been selected on the shores of Lake Arrowhead, California, and the pioneer's ax was loud on the slopes of the San Bernardino Range. Then weeks passed without any word and a horrible premonition seized me. By now, I thought, the first crop of Capeharts should have been harvested and stored, and the settlers have successfully withstood a nocturnal raid by a fierce finance company. I could see the brave little band, the men gaunt from lack of caviar, the women desperately hoarding the last precious drop of *Arpège*. My heart sank and I lived only for the reassurance the next mail would bring from Mr. Oliver.

It came an hour ago—a big, bulky envelope bursting with maps, sketches, and a breathless prose poem by the founding father outlining the future of the settlement. "This is a birds-eye view of the proposed Writers' Colony," he began, his words tumbling over each other in his excitement. "Let's flutter down to the rocky point at the bottom center of our map. . . . We'll pause at the first cabin on our right, the one with the twin fireplaces. This houses a writer and his writer wife. Each have their own workplace, and 'tis said, though busy, they sometimes meet between meals to use the dictionary in the library that joins these twin think-shops." At this last tinkling phrase my glasses misted over with emotion and I believe I would have fallen but for the fact that I was already lying down. "Leaving our writer friend, we turn back towards the Lake along a little fenced path and we climb over stiles as it leads us down alongside of the store. The store is the building next to the Inn and the Inn is the building with the stagecoach out in front. . . . In the store you will be able to buy one of those nice old glazed brown bean pots—or a black iron kettle—for your fireplace, or a powder horn to hang up with that squirrel rifle over the door. . . . After crossing the little bridge at the creek we look up and see another lucky writer building his log hideout. He must have come from Michigan—in a little garden patch he has set out a crabapple tree, and some old Eastern lilacs. Well, let's mosey down to the water's edge and climb up on that old rail fence, and rest—and watch the reflection of the sunset on our little cove. Beautiful sight, isn't it? Take a deep breath of that good old fragrant pine air. Hmmm—there's a whiff of bacon in that air, too. Come on, let's get going; it's time to eat. . . ."

I'll tell you what, old man. Why don't *you* boys run along and eat, and if I feel well enough, I'll join you later? And by the way, slip this baffle into my mailbox on your way out, will you? There's a dear.

Why Boys Leave Home

EVERY WOMAN worth her salt, and even the few unsalted ones I have known, cherishes somewhere in her heart midway between the auricle and the ventricle a lovely, pastel-tinted dream. Maid or matron, she longs to dress up her man in a velvet smoking jacket and red morocco slippers, plant him in his favorite easy chair with a pipe and a rattling good detective story, and then, the moment his eyes freeze over, launch into a catalogue of bargains available at the stores. My own chocolate drop is no exception. One evening a while ago, I tottered in from a grueling afternoon at the bookmaker's and collapsed heavily in my Morris chair. I barely had time to sluice my larynx with a healing emollient of honey and orange bitters, and a drop of cognac to allay the insupportable sweetness, before the nightly overture struck up.

"Well, I vum," began my helpmate, unfolding her newspaper. "Do you remember those cunning little doilies Sandra Vermifuge bought two years ago at Neiman & Marcus, in Dallas? She paid a dollar forty-nine for them, and here they are at McCreery's for only a dollar forty-three. I can't wait to see her face!"

"Neither can I," I giggled. "Let's call her up and tease her! Where does she live now?"

"In Spokane, I think," said my wife doubtfully. "But you don't really intend——"

"Why not?" I urged. "Oh, come on, it's only a twenty-three-dollar toll call!" My proposal was received with an icy silence that melted forty-five seconds later, just as I had relaxed my neck muscles and begun a realistic imitation of a transcontinental truck puffing up a grade.

"Macy's is holding its annual clearance of barbecue aprons," the Voice resumed. "We've got four, but I don't think you can have too many barbecue aprons, do you? . . . And look at this: there's a sacrifice of poplin-covered steamer chairs at Altman's, eighty-nine dollars and ninety-eight cents, only twenty-two to a customer. . . . Genuine quilted-rayon cheese strainers, marked down to four fifty-four. . . . Now here's something we really need! . . . Are you awake?"

"Urg," I replied, to indicate I was drinking in every word.

"GIMBELS JACKS UP YOUR CAR!" she read breathlessly. "GIMBELS COVERS UP YOUR CAR. If you're going to Florida, leave your car protected, so it will stay spick-and-span until you return. Jack it up on our plywood jacks—they'll hold an eight-ton truck for the duration. Then cover it from stem to stern with our paper coverall to keep out dust, soot, grit and grime; it's sturdy kraft paper——"

"Listen!" I roared. "I like the car the way it is! I like it down there in the country with mushrooms in the clutch and chickens roosting in the glove compartment! And if you think I'm going to travel sixty-four miles in the dead of winter to dress up a '37 Plymouth in a paper tent, you can jolly well——"

"Of course not, gingerbread boy," agreed Circe soothingly, "but it can't hurt if I stop in tomorrow and look at it, can it?"

Which may explain how I came to reel into the railroad station at Frogtown, New Jersey, yesterday morning in a subarctic dawn, my spectacles opaque with steam and my pygmy frame bent double under a massive carton. The freight agent squirted tobacco juice over my shoes in welcome.

"Back for the summer, eh?" he inquired. "Say, you certainly look awful. What are those big circles under your eyes?"

"Glasses," I said evenly. "What the hell do you think they are?"

"You never got 'em drinkin' milk," he guffawed, slapping his thigh. "Say, what's in that there box?"

"A body," I snapped. "The body of a freight agent with a long nose that he kept sticking into other people's business." There was a short, pregnant silence during which our eyes stood toe-to-toe and slugged it out. Then, humming a nonchalant air, I sauntered into a snowdrift outside and dawdled a scant hour and a half wondering how to cover the seven miles to my duchy without a car. At last a friendly chicken farmer drew up, attracted by my humorous carrot nose, stovepipe hat and lumps of coal simulating buttons.

"Ain't no room up front here," he said hospitably, leaning out of the warm, cozy cab of his truck, "but you can ride back there with them pullets."

For the first couple of miles, it was a novel experience to travel with a boutonnière of Rhode Island Reds pecking at my cravat, but eventually their silly feminine chatter bored me, and averting my face, I drank in great healing lungfuls of the exhaust. With the perfect sense of timing that characterizes everything I do, I arranged matters so that my chariot was exactly abreast of the post office as a group of neighborhood louts emerged.

"Pretty good-sized capon you raised there, Zeb," they complimented my ferryman. "Figger on butcherin' him now or feedin' him through the winter?"

Their good-natured derision was infectious, and averting my face, I drank in great healing lungfuls of the pullets. Soon, however, the spires of my château came into sight and I vaulted nimbly into a puddle, slashing a jagged rent in my overcoat, and trudged up the glare ice to Lackluster Farm. Time had wrought few changes in the old place; one or two chimneys had fallen down and passing sportsmen had blown out every pane of glass in the windows, but there was nothing amiss that fifty thousand dollars would not cure.

Divesting myself of my coat to insure a spanking case of pneumonia, I gamely caught up the carton and staggered to the barn where the car was housed. Fortunately, there was no need to waste time opening doors, as the wind had obligingly torn them from their tracks. The trip along the dark threshing floor was uneventful, except that I adroitly involved myself in a rope hanging from the beams and conceived the ridiculous notion that someone was trying to garrote me. I emitted a few piercing cries, however, and it shook itself loose. The car itself seemed more streamlined than I remembered it, until I realized that parties unknown had removed the tires, along with the wheels. I rarely give way to my feelings, but in the irritation of the moment, I gave those axles a kick they will remember for many a day to come. As soon as my foot stopped throbbing, I routed out an old broom and transferred the dust and wheat chaff which had settled down over the body to my own. Then, arms akimbo, I shrewdly laid out my plan of campaign.

The first thing to do, I said to myself, was to get the car up on the wooden jacks. To accomplish this, I would need a stout tire jack, which must be in the luggage compartment. The key to the luggage compartment, though, was on my bureau sixty-four miles away, where I had prudently left it. Ergo, I must force the lock—child's play to one whose knowledge of mechanics was a household word for ten feet around. I procured a pinch bar from the toolroom, inserted it under the door of the luggage compartment, and heaved my weight downward as outlined in first-year physics.

After picking myself up from the floor, I twisted my handkerchief into a makeshift tourniquet and decided that the wooden jacks would be superfluous anyhow, as the car already stood staunchly on its transmission. The next step, hence, was to envelop it in the paper coverall. I clawed up the carton and eventually succeeded in setting up the coverall, though several times the wind sweeping through the barn bore me off into the fields like a box kite.

"Now, easy does it," I said cunningly—I had reached the stage where I was addressing myself aloud—and holding the coverall above my head like Paul and Virginia fleeing before the storm, I crept up over the top of the car and dropped it neatly into place. Unluckily, this left me pinned on my stomach in the dark, slowly throttling under sturdy kraft paper;

and acting on a sudden obscure impulse, I decided not to linger. I went through the side of the coverall biting, gouging and scratching, and when I hit the lane, I kept on going. The natives are still talking about the meteor covered with chicken feathers that flashed across the Delaware River yesterday afternoon. And the minute he gets his breath back, the meteor's going to do a little talking himself—to Mrs. Meteor.

Creepy-time Gal

SHOULD YOU OPEN somebody else's mail by mistake during the next few weeks and find, dimpling up at you, a brisk little insect that looks like a tangle of black pipe-cleaners, there are a couple of things you can do. One is to shinny down the waterspout like crazy; the other, if you haven't a waterspout, is to shinny down where you think it ought to be. Only, for God's sake, don't be a purist. Just *shinny*.

It's not that I'm especially psychic or anything—the notion of mail-order insects is set forth with freezing clarity in an article called "Selling Tarantulas," by W-W-Weldon D.

Woodson (don't mind if I stammer a little; you'd stammer too if you had seen those photographs), in a recent issue of *Pets* magazine. Mr. Woodson has found a man in Los Angeles named Raymond Thorp, who sells tarantulas, black widows and scorpions to people who haven't got tarantulas, black widows and scorpions. "Only this morning," Mr. Thorp informed Mr. Woodson, "a dozen 'black' or Hentzii tarantulas (not males) started on their journey to a gentleman in British Columbia; a dozen of the silver-tipped Avicularia to a doctor in Minnesota; a half-dozen of the same species to a man in Ohio; a trio of dark-brown, silky Steindachneri to a lady in Florida; a quintet of reddish-brown Eurypelma to a Canadian museum of zoology." I think Mr. Thorp expresses himself the least bit ambiguously. The phrase "started on their journey" conjures up a picture of a bevy of giggling tarantulas in ruffled organdy and wide-awake straw hats fussing over lunch baskets and teasing the conductor. What Mr. Thorp intended to convey was simply the fact that thirty-eight assorted tarantulas were clearing through the mails while he stood there chewing the fat, and that's right where I started sweating freely.

Mr. Woodson, whom I somehow visualize as standing on one foot and scratching nervously throughout the interview, nevertheless managed to inquire what people wanted with such creatures anyway. "Mere wanton curiosity accounts for the great majority of orders," Thorp answered with a smile (occasioned, no doubt, by the Eurypelma he saw snuggling on Mr. Woodson's collar). "Next in volume comes from those who use them for window display advertising, and one can readily imagine the crowds lured to a store window filled with tarantulas, black widows, scorpions, and centipedes; some fighting, others hatching out and eating their young." I must be stiff with sales resistance, for I can just as readily imagine myself lured to a store at the other end of town, cheerfully paying through the nose to miss such an engaging spectacle. Not so Mr. Thorp, however, who says proudly, "In my eyes there is nothing more interesting than this spider [the black tarantula, Eurypelma Hentzii], which, despite its looks, is so meek that a two-year-old baby can handle it with safety." Anybody who puts a tarantula in a crib with a two-year-old baby must be crazy, if he cares anything about the tarantula; this is strictly a case of diamond cut diamond. I can't go along with Mr. Thorp any further than that, though, and his attitude toward his fourteen-year-old son, Carroll, seems to me to be one of affection tinged with the sort of sangfroid you might display toward live bait. If you are an excitable father who sends for a bronchoscopist every time your child swallows a grape, get a load of Carroll:

> He is frequently sent out on a hurry-up mission to bring in as many as fifty spiders in an afternoon. . . . The tarantulas are distributed about over his clothing where they cling very nicely until brought to book in our menagerie.

John Greenleaf Whittier or no, the next barefoot boy with cheeks of tan who tries to thumb a ride from me within fifty miles of Los Angeles gets a Stilson wrench across the knuckles.

The further one ventures into *Pets* magazine, the better one understands why its title was changed several months ago from *Popular Pets* to just plain *Pets*. Picking up another issue with a forked stick, I ran full tilt into a dithyrambic essay by Renée B. Stiles, called "I Love Snakes." Not "Who's Afraid of Snakes?" mind you, or "Snakes Roll Right off My Knife," but the good old simple declarative—the way I feel about Madeleine Carroll. And lest any doubting Thomas try to confute her, the author has had herself photographed pitching woo at one of her favorites, an eight-foot Florida Indigo who sleeps in her bedroom. "He will take meat right out of my hands," avers Mrs. Stiles in a perfect frenzy of devotion. Girlie, that's practically an epigram.

Mrs. Stiles houses in her Minneapolis home a collection of more than fifty poisonous and nonpoisonous specimens, but the eternal feminine in her prefers one Peck's Bad Boy:

> I believe that the most interesting snake in my whole collection is my 5½-foot Siamese Hooded Cobra and I like him because, unlike other North American poisonous snakes, he is aggressive.

It's only a summer romance, evidently, for she says elsewhere:

I would like to own a coral snake, but because this type is dangerously small and difficult to watch, I am afraid that my neighbors would object rather strenuously.

This would imply that until now the neighbors have been serenading Mrs. Stiles with mandolins and sending over old-fashioned molasses cookies, which I find hard to believe. You can bet your life people don't mouse around Mrs. Stiles' home pinching the drapes and hissing, "Tattletale gray, my dear." Not unless they want a cottonmouth in their ruching.

If concern for pets is any index of a warm, generous nature, Mrs. Stiles must be the very paragon of a hostess, and yet there is one passage in her article that makes me think her weekend guests would do well to avoid eating between meals. "In my kitchen," she relates, "I have a white-enameled reptilian apartment house which consists of six compartments, one atop the other, with screen front and sliding doors to permit individual handling and feeding. On the top story is 5½ feet of untamed Western Diamondback Rattler. Next below is a handsome Texas Indigo. A Minnesota Timber and a Montana Prairie Rattlesnake share the lower quarters, while my Gila Monster and Iguana strike up a strange acquaintance the fourth story down. Then there is my African Ball Python and finally my Bull Snake and a blotched Chicken Snake." Here is one household where the temptation to sneak down and raid the icebox should be fought tooth and nail. Fill up at the table, even make a pig of yourself, but don't start casting sheep's eyes at that chestnut dressing when Ruby removes it to the kitchen. You're sitting pretty. And so am I, as long as I can stay up here on top of this ridgepole. Of course, the slates get pretty hot in the daytime and about all I can see is birds, but say, I *like* birds. I wouldn't mind having a bird for a pet—if I ever have another pet.

Garnish Your Face with Parsley and Serve

On a balmy summer evening in Los Angeles some years ago, heavy with the scent of mimosa and crispy-fried noodles from the Chinese quarter, I happened to be a member of the small, select audience of cocaine peddlers, package thieves, and assorted strays at the Cozy Theater that witnessed the world première of a remarkable motion picture called *The Sex Maniac*. Most of the production, I grieve to say, is little more than a blur in my memory, but one scene still stands out with cameo-like clarity. Into the consulting room of a fairly mad physician, whose name I somehow remember as

Lucas Membrane, hurtled a haggard middle-aged woman, towing her husband, a psychotic larrikin about seven feet tall. The doctor examined the patient cursorily through a pocket lens, inspected his tongue, and, muttering "Just as I feared—dementia praecox," inoculated him intravenously with an icing gun like those commonly found in French bakeries. The patient slowly expanded, gnashing his teeth, until his head grazed the ceiling. Then he darted into the next room, where a luscious showgirl in a diaphanous shift unaccountably lay asleep on a slab, and, booming like a bittern, hustled her off into the canebrake. His wife and Dr. Membrane stared after him, shaking their heads in mild perplexity. "Well, Doc," observed the former, inflecting her words in the classic manner of Miss Beatrice Lillie, "I've seen some pretty . . . strange . . . experiments in my time, but *this* . . . is tops."

I was tempted to echo these sentiments yesterday when, in the Sunday edition of the Newark *Star-Ledger* which I received as lagniappe with fifteen cents' worth of sour tomatoes on Division Street, I ran across an arresting article on various home beauty treatments evolved by Hollywood personalities. It appears that, far from favoring expensive skin foods and massage creams, our reigning film favorites prefer cosmetics drawn from their own kitchen shelves. Like Dolores Moran, for instance. Any discussion of lovely Hollywood elbows would be incomplete without a reference to hers; I myself recall more than one such discussion that seemed frustrated and sterile because no reference was made to Miss Moran's elbows. To keep them trig and alluring, the blond starlet rests them on two halves of a lemon for twenty minutes while she rehearses her lines, then rubs them satin-smooth with olive oil. Julie Bishop preserves her hands by rolling them in oatmeal (which, of course, she discards before playing her more romantic love scenes), and Ida Lupino safeguards an already creamy complexion with a poultice of powdered milk. Urging her readers to branch out for themselves, the beauty editor of the *Star-Ledger* appends several other recipes of a similar homely nature, notably a hand pack of corn meal and benzoin, an egg whipped up in lemon juice to rejuvenate tired or muddy faces, and a flocculent suspension of cornstarch in boiling water as an emollient for leathery skins.

What with a soaring luxury tax and a shrinking supply of cosmetics, it was inevitable that Elizabeth Arden would be supplanted by the grocery counter, but I am none too sure of the effect on the masculine gender. I foresee almost certain repercussions in the divorce courts and the Sunday-evening radio tribunals, and I offer the following *mise en scène* as a horoscope of what to expect shortly over any major network:

[*Scene: A radio station. John J. Antennae, spiritual father to millions, broods remotely before his microphone, pondering the philosophy of Ralph Waldo Trine and waiting for the announcer to complete his commercial. Fox-nosed, sallow, closely related to God on his mother's side, Antennae has been by turns an insurance technician, reception clerk in a cut-rate mortuary, and used-car salesman. From the side he dimly resembles a spider, an effect he tries to counteract with a ghastly veneer of benevolence.*]

ANNOUNCER: . . . So why not back up our boys in the steaming jungles of New Guinea by chewing Respighi's Bubble Gum, that amazing new blend of chicle, old tea leaves and pine shavings? Remember, folks, maladroit tests by wool-gathering scientists have shown that Respighi's contains no single ingredient that could kill a horse, and even if it did, the hydrochloric acid in your system will dissolve anything. And now, Mr. Antennae, the case of Mr. M. W.

ANTENNAE (*nasally*): Step up, please. (*Milton Wefers, a dispirited taxpayer in his mid-thirties, falters to the podium.*) Very well, sir, tell us your story. (*Wefers blubbers wordlessly.*) Come, come, tears aren't going to help. Here, take my hand. Now then.

WEFERS (*brokenly*): Mr. Antennae, I first met my present wife in high school.

ANTENNAE: Just a moment. Am I to understand that you first met your present wife in high school?

WEFERS: That is correct.

ANTENNAE (*sharply*): You mean you had not met this

woman—this little lady to whom you have pledged the most sacred vow the human voice can utter—previous to the time you speak of? Answer yes or no.

WEFERS: No. Well, shortly after we were married—seventeen years, five months, and four days, to be exact—I started in noticing that this party, that is, my wife, was covered with cracker meal.

ANTENNAE: Cracker meal? You don't mean Crainquebille, do you?

WEFERS (*lymphatically*): Crainquebille? What's that?

ANTENNAE: It's a story by Anatole France.

WEFERS: How could my wife be covered with a story by Anatole France?

ANTENNAE (*waspishly*): I'm the one who's asking the questions around here, Percy.

ANNOUNCER: Yes, Mr. Antennae—and friends in our listening audience—do *you* ever ask yourself the question: What am I doing to keep myself sweet and wholesome for those boys in the steaming jungles of New Guinea? It's your patriotic duty as an American to protect the home front with Respighi's, that yummy, gummy confection that irradiates the vocal cords and promotes pharyngeal fun!

ANTENNAE: All right now, go ahead with your problem.

WEFERS: So like I say, Mr. Antennae, it made me nervous my wife always wearing cracker crumbs at the table. I mean it got on my nerves. It was like living in the same house with a breaded veal cutlet.

ANTENNAE (*silkily*): I see. I take it you've had considerable experience sharing your residence with breaded veal cutlets?

WEFERS: Well, no, but I—

ANTENNAE: Tell me, young man, have you ever had any —ah—psychic disturbances? Ever been confined to an institution?

WEFERS: No, sir.

ANTENNAE: Never received a blow on the head, to the best of your recollection?

WEFERS: No, sir. Well, pretty soon I begun to watch her and I saw all kinds of things that made me suspicious. Every time I come home at night, why she would have her nose in a grapefruit.

ANTENNAE: How do you mean?

WEFERS: I mean she would be lying down with this grapefruit on her countenance. She said it took out the wrinkles.

ANNOUNCER: Yes, folks, and speaking of wrinkles, here's a new one! Did you know that every stick of Respighi's Bubble Gum is subjected to six hundred pounds of live steam to bake in the invigorating freshness of the great north woods? The next time you're in a lumber yard, make this test for yourself: whittle off the end of a fresh spruce plank and chew it to a pulp. That same zestful tang of turpentine and resin comes to you in each factory-fresh packet of Respighi's, the Friendlier Gum, chosen all-time favorite by our boys in the steaming jungles of New Guinea!

ANTENNAE: Now, my friend, continue your story. You claim that this behavior on the part of your loved one caused you a feeling of anguish?

WEFERS: It did, Mr. Antennae. (*Sobbing*) I was a loving husband at all times; I was always bringing her little bags of fruit and candy and kissing her on the nape of the neck—

ANTENNAE (*hastily*): Yes, yes, no details, please. Go on with your narrative.

WEFERS: One Sunday morning I went in the kitchen and found her making some fried eggs. I thought they were for my breakfast, but instead of putting them on my plate, she placed them on her chin, like a kind of a hot compress.

ANTENNAE: You discussed the incident with her?

WEFERS: She stated that it would give her a firm, well-molded, youthful throat. Then I started to take some farina out of the double boiler, but she said she was saving it for her forehead. She also told me she planned to use my marmalade under her eyes to banish crow's-feet.

ANTENNAE: What was the upshot of these actions?

WEFERS: Well, I couldn't stand it any longer, so I went down to the public library.

ANTENNAE: To think things out, is that it?

WEFERS: No, sir. To reread a story by Melville Davisson Post called "Corpus Delicti."

ANTENNAE: Oh? What was this story about?

WEFERS (*bashfully*): I'd rather not say.

ANTENNAE: What transpired after that between you and your wife?

WEFERS: I'd rather not say.

ANTENNAE: You seem to have gotten pretty close-mouthed all of a sudden.

WEFERS: Yup.

ANTENNAE: Since the Sunday you speak of, has there been any substantial change in your wife?

WEFERS: Oh, boy.

ANTENNAE: Have you noticed anything out of the ordinary in the household?

WEFERS: Well, there was a funny smell of nitric acid in the bathroom, but it went away after a while.

ANTENNAE: And what, precisely, brings you here tonight? What is your problem?

WEFERS: Well, Mr. Antennae, I tell you. A couple of weeks ago I got interested in a certain party, a hostess in a rumba school. She returns my affection and we were wondering if we should get married.

ANTENNAE: You're sure your wife doesn't stand in the way?

WEFERS: Positive.

ANTENNAE: Well, my boy, I'm going to give you youngsters the sort of advice I don't believe I've ever given anyone before. *Go* to this person, look deep into your hearts, I beg of you, and when you've found the answer—*if* you have the courage in yourselves to face the questions that *need* answering, mind you—*make* up your minds, won't you? . . . You will? . . . (*Emotionally*) God bless you!

ANNOUNCER: Folks, have you ever stopped to realize how barren the world would be without a sticky glutinous blob adhering to your dentition? Do you know that in the steaming jungles of New Guinea, your boys consider Respighi's Bubble Gum their number one ration? They're counting on you, Respighi-chewers; don't let them down. It's *so* juicy—*so* tasty—and golly, we've got *so* much of it on hand!

CURTAIN

Your Move, General Sarnoff

Our hostess mumbled so when she introduced us that perhaps I'd better identify myself all over again. I am a fairly typical Yankee in a coonskin cap and linsey-woolsey who looks like Gary Cooper, sings like Frank Sinatra and dances like Fred Astaire, and I'd like to say a few words about radio. The hell with it—there, I've said it. I hate to sound sulky—though everyone tells me that when I do, I'm a dead ringer for Simone Simon—but wouldn't you think there'd be a spot in radio for a man of my talents? Well, there isn't. Ever since last Tuesday, when I made my debut on the air, my phone hasn't rung once.

The whole tawdry affair began one afternoon about a week ago in the office of a lady known as Aunt Lou, who broadcasts a housewives' hour each morning. As my eyes swam into focus, they lit on a frail old soul of twenty-seven, dressed in tight black satin, bent over me, hungrily surveying my cherry-red lips. Although her ostensible purpose was to persuade me to appear as a guest on her program, there was no mistaking the look of yearning in her eyes.

"P-please," I faltered, disentangling my hand from her hair, "you mustn't; I'm a married man. Besides, how do I know you'll still feel the same after—after I've appeared on your program?"

"Of course I will, you silly little goose," she purred. "Come on. What do you say? How about next Tuesday?"

I felt my strength ebbing as her hypnotic pupils bored into my very core, but with a last desperate effort, I squirmed out of her embrace, thrust a chair in her path, and raced to the nearest elocution school to prepare for my ordeal.

On the advice of my teacher, an unfrocked basso who assured me that I was another Chaliapin, though stingier, I spent the ensuing three days before a mirror with a medicated lozenge in my mouth, intoning "a-e-i-o-u" to achieve deep pear tones. I also laid in a small store of autographed photos to reward my fans with some trifling keepsake when they swarmed about me after the show. The news that I was invading radio, naturally, burst like a bombshell on the Gay White Way; the jealous resentment of my competitors was comical in the extreme. Jack Benny and Raymond Gram Swing contented themselves with the coolest of nods when we met in Bustanoby's or Reisenweber's. One night at home, I casually let fall a hint to the family circle that I was making my radio bow in a few days.

"Oh, by the by," I remarked casually, flicking an infinitesimal speck of ash from my lapel—I always keep a lapel with an infinitestimal speck of ash on it for such emergencies—"don't let me oversleep Tuesday. I'm broadcasting, you know. I mean, that's the morning of my broadcast. And if anybody calls me on Tuesday morning, I'm broadcasting."

"Is that so?" my bride marveled. "Look, run down to the drugstore and get me a cheese sandwich, will you?" I pretended not to have heard, and stifling an elaborate yawn, ran down to the drugstore for her cheese sandwich.

The fateful hour found me a vision of loveliness at the microphone, chewing a pebble in the manner of Demosthenes and declaiming Whittier's "Snowbound" under my breath. As the program ran only an hour, I planned to limit myself to but fifty minutes of actual speech, feeling that since it was my trial flight, I must be modest. The musical chime sounded, and Aunt Lou, in a broad cracker dialect reminiscent of Lew Primrose's Minstrels, launched into a commercial lasting nineteen minutes. I cleared my throat to speak, but she gave me a flinty look and began another. At the end of forty-seven minutes, she was midway through a panegyric on Winograd's Dual-Purpose Peanut Butter and

I was a dead pigeon. My lips were parched and my eyes had receded into my head like a prospector's in Death Valley. Suddenly she broke off and switched me on without troubling to introduce me.

" 'Lo, folks," I croaked. "Well, it certainly is a small world —a microcosm, you might say. I am reminded of the story of the two Irishmen, Patrocosm and Microcosm——"

"That's all, dear," chuckled Aunt Lou. "And now, we've just time for a hundred and eighty-two more commercials before signing off. Ladies, why not try cooking with Proskauer's Self-Perpetuating Floor Wax?"

An hour later, the president of the network looked up in surprise as I strode into his sanctum. He was opening his mouth to fawn on me when I halted him with an imperious gesture. Brushing aside his offers of a town car, an investment trust and a harem of Circassian girls, I tendered my resignation to take effect instanter. If you ever go in there, my hat is still on the right as you enter, on the hook. And so is my radio career, if anybody should ask you.

Quiet, Please

I AM NO MORE superstitious than the next man (the next man happens to hail from the Cameroons and is crouched on his hams shrinking his uncle's head over a slow fire), but, as one forced to do a considerable amount of travelling, I carry not only a large accident policy but a small St. Christopher's medal. With this figurative two-way stretch, I manage to get adequate coverage on what is, after all, a flabby middle-aged risk. Such protection, however, is on the purely physical plane; up to press time no agency, whether human or divine, has been able to devise an effective talisman against spiritual hazards. Like bores, for example. It may be only hypertension, but I could swear there are more bores around than when I was a boy.

I am apparently one of those natural victims who act on bores like vintage champagne, exciting and inflaming them to fresh excesses. The mere sound of my footfall in the entresol is a challenge to their previous records. Miss Tennyson Jesse has suggested that just as there are born murderers, there are also unfortunate creatures called murderees, whose destiny it is to be ruthlessly expunged. Why is it more unreasonable to assume that I may have some fatal attraction for bores, some ghastly allure, which brings out everything most shameful in them? If this were a simple hammer-and-anvil relationship instead of one involving living tissue, I could face the future with fortitude. But of late the bores have been increasing in malignity as well as number, like buzzards wheeling over a magnificent stricken stag, and the incidental music is developing a feverish, crescendo quality I don't care for in the least. No, sir, I don't like it for bob-nuts.

In any catalogue of bores, it would be impossible to undervalue the importance of the accidental, or suddenly vocal, type. This is the man whose friends have said of him for years, in a comfortable tone of voice, "Well, I guess the cat's got Vernon's tongue." Their supposition is only partially correct, for the cat has it in escrow. One evening, before attending a meeting at which I am invariably present,

Vernon, a total abstainer, is induced to try some curaçao or Fiori d'Alpini. "Why, this isn't strong," he giggles. "What's that little tree doing in there?" By the time the chairman's gavel descends, Vernon is seated in the front row wearing a boozy, foolish smile, his mouth ringed with the last remaining crystals from the bottle. Right in the middle of the agenda, as the report of the nominating committee is being rushed through, Vernon abruptly blows his top. Bolting to his feet with a reek of cordial you could smell five miles down wind, he casts off his cocoon and emerges as the great parliamentarian. "Point of order, Mr. Chairman!" he trumpets. "Before we move the question, let's throw the discussion open to the floor. I feel there are certain abuses confronting the membership . . ." The audience is so dumfounded at this show of eloquence that fully five minutes elapse before a handcar is dispatched to overtake the runaway; by which time it is too late, for Vernon is surrounded by a circle of toadies pressing the aldermanic mace on him and assuring him he is the equal of the elder Pitt. From then on he becomes the self-appointed Opposition whip, tabling resolutions, canvassing the back benches, and huddling in cloakrooms hissing phrases like "sinking fund" and "quid pro quo." He won't stop until he gets to the State Legislature, and that's okay by me.

An even more infuriating kind is the bore who plays his cards so close to his chest that it is badly abraded. This variety has decided that if he opens his mouth he may commit himself, and hence has withdrawn from the world like a Trappist monk—without, however, having the decency to announce it. One enters his society as unsuspecting as a tourist who had never heard the gossip about Count Dracula would enter Transylvania. Extremely gregarious, the silent bore is found wherever fun is at its maddest, his limbs utterly relaxed and his hooded, unwinking eye fixed on his prey. His presence produces an effect contrary to what might be supposed. As the pressure increases, the dupe experiences a gloomy hypnosis and an intolerable compulsion to babble. Hoary old anecdotes, the most tender confidences, fragments of nursery rhyme, gush from his lips—anything to fight off the icy constriction tightening around his heart. Lost in an Arctic waste, he cries out in vain to his companions, pursues mirages, flaps his arms, and finally collapses, sobbing brokenly, into unconsciousness. As a result, he is stricken from the rolls as a very bad drunk by his hostess, who simultaneously invites the silent bore to drop in the following afternoon and inspect her collection of early American knishes.

A few gifted newspapermen have succeeded in becoming bores, chiefly through grit rather than any kind of "luck." I have in mind one who at thirty-three can look back over a life packed with incident, and does so with dogged persistence. Though he ruefully admits he missed the death of Stanford White—he was bending over to dust his shoe at the time—he has been present at every major homicide since.

He chanced to be strolling arm-in-arm with Rosenthal when the gambler was obliterated by Gyp the Blood and his associates, he had just filled an inside straight as Arnold Rothstein entered the Park Central, and he was helping Joseph Elwell count his bridge winnings when a veiled lady was announced. Such widely divergent personalities as Monk Eastman and Isadora Duncan, Starr Faithful and Rasputin, made him legatee for their spiciest secrets. No wonder that after a career so charged with action he should have retired to a quiet backwater like 21 West 52nd Street to conduct a perpetual seminar for a group of the more advanced students. Does a horrid civic scandal impend? He will cheerfully recall the Tweed Ring, the Stavisky affair, the manipulations of the Huey Long dynasty. Are the police of three states baffled by the Mad Butcher of Shrewsbury Run? Seated a thousand miles from the scene, he furnishes a theory worthy of Mycroft Holmes, based on personal observation of Fritz Haarmann and Landru. He may not be able to remember his own name by curfew time, but it's a cinch he mentions everybody else's before stumbling off to his date with Hedy Lamarr.

And speaking of picture people . . . or am I boring you?

Yoo-Hoo, Mr. Ectoplasm!

I MAY BE WRONG, and always am, but when kiddies from six to sixty, who have been sinking their pin money into diabolos, pyrography sets, and glass marbles containing little lambs get one peep at a booklet I received from abroad this morning, they are going to be very fickle indeed with their hobbies. As a kiddie who has gone along for years believing that the catalogue of the Sex Shop in Kobe, Japan, was just about tops in curiosa, I may as well turn in my badge and register a sporting proposition. If the new spring and summer catalogue of the Psychic Stores, 548 High Road, Chiswick, London, W.4, doesn't give you the fantods, I will crawl on all fours from Bethnal Green to Seven Dials. The betting fancy can find my representative, Colonel Geraldine, any evening at Mr. Theophilus Godall's cigar divan in Greek Street, Soho, where details will be arranged over a quiet cheroot.

The Psychic Stores are a depot stocked with every known appliance for communicating with the Beyond, short of razors, revolvers and veronal. Such standard impedimenta as séance trumpets, luminous slates, planchettes, and ouija boards are overshadowed by more elaborate mechanisms like the Electrograph, the Séance Vibrator, the Receptograph, and Skotograph Plates. Some of these cost a pretty penny and demand at least six credits at M.I.T. from the operator. The Electrograph, for instance, is a job about the size of a portable gramophone fitted out with keyboards, ground-glass screens, and batteries. After the spirits are sufficiently softened up, even those who were illiterate on this side of Jordan may be counted on to type rapid messages to their friends in the séance. "The crowning test of the Electrograph"—I quote the catalogue—"is to receive answers to unspoken questions, a result which cannot be explained by normal science and which therefore proves 'Spiritualism.' " The editor of the *Scientific American* will do well to button his lip and withdraw that insolent ten-thousand-dollar offer.

The catalogue opens with a stringent warning to users of its appliances. Two attempts per week to penetrate the

Other Side are all the traffic will bear. "Too frequent attempts overtax your psychic gifts, whilst irregular times make it impossible for regular spirit helpers to set the time apart to assist you. They may have other business to attend to, unless you make your regular appointment in advance." This dredges up a pretty unattractive picture of the hereafter, with time clocks, Kardex systems, and, for all we know, conferences in which ghostly Corona-Coronas are chewed. I don't know about their branch offices in the next world, but the Psychic Stores tolerate no nonsense on this plane—at least so far as their merchandising is concerned. However ethereal their wares, they conduct everything on a very realistic basis: "POSTAGE is free (except abroad). POSTAGE ABROAD is 1/- extra per parcel." You'd think anybody who could tap the cosmic telephone line wouldn't have to resort to delivery by parcel post.

Although they try not to play favorites, the Psychic Stores are especially proud of their Psychaloid Séance Trumpet. "Psychaloid Trumpets," we find, "are manufactured with 'Psychaloid,' which in turn is made from celluloid. 'Psychaloid' is the easiest material which spirits may handle, or rap upon, and is the ideal material for construction of Séance Trumpets. It has recently been discovered by the manufacturers of this trumpet." It has also recently been discovered by a bunch of boys working in an old barn in Delaware, who style themselves the Dupont Cellulose Corporation but who are obviously charlatans. The present writer has been using a comb made of their compound, as well as a shoehorn, but so far no spirits have been detected handling or rapping upon either his hair or his oxfords.

Under the sharp query "Are You a Skotograph Medium?" is an explanation of this remarkable form of clairvoyance. For one-and-six, the Stores sell "a singly-wrapped, specially sensitive 'skotorapide' skotograph plate. Carry it, without unwrapping, in your pocket for a day, then take it to your local chemist to be developed. There may be pictures or spirit writing on it." The one time I ever carried a photographic plate in this manner the results were even more gratifying. I got a perfectly peachy snapshot of the inside of my pocket, together with a montage of bits of Hershey bar, thread, and a substance resembling Canton ginger. Inasmuch as I never carry Canton ginger on my person (of course, it's different if I happen to *be* in Canton or something), I had the substance analyzed, and sure enough back came the report "Canton ginger." I wish somebody would use this little experience of mine as a testimonial. I don't know anybody in the Canton-ginger game, and all I got out of the Hershey people when I submitted it was a rather ill-tempered letter. The Psychic Stores are a fool if they don't sign me up. I can be had for a pair of their "Kilnascrene Glasses," which the catalogue describes as follows: "These resemble a pair of motorcyclist's goggles, with the exception that the lenses are of a dark glass, of very special quality. The glasses are worn for three minutes, and after removal the wearer may find he is clairvoyant." I occasionally visit a small spiritualist circle which meets in licensed premises under the Herald Tribune Building; inevitably I come away from the séances with eye trouble because of spoons and pretzels getting into my eyes. A pair of stout Kilnascrenes would be just my candy, and if I wore them for six minutes instead of three, I could get double vision at half the present expense.

On second thought, perhaps I'm letting myself go too cheaply. What our circle really needs is the Psychic Stores' special Séance Vibrator, described thus:

> The Séance Vibrator will improve the results at any meeting for psychic development or séance, beyond recognition. It keeps all the sitters at the same rate of vibration, and therefore in harmony, without diverting or interfering with their mental concentration, as does music. It consists of a battery, an electric vibrator, contained in a small mahogany casquet, and operated by an external switch. Different tones are obtained by standing the instrument on its base, or either side, and by resting it upon wood, or upon the carpet. It emits a very pleasing deep soft note. Keep it "on" throughout your circles. When the Vibrator is in use, singing or music is unnecessary and the inconvenient and upsetting business of manipulating a gramophone in the dark is avoided. Battery replacements may be purchased at your local bicycle shop. The Vibrator costs about a penny per hour to run.

And just in case you think this is too good to be true, the cost is only ten-and-six. Where are you going to get a decent massage for eight people for two dollars and sixty-five cents, let alone an evening's chat with the infinite? It doesn't even have to be a new model; I'm sure we could manage with a salesman's demonstrator, couldn't we, fellows? . . . Oh, Psychic Stores! . . . Calling Psychic Stores! . . . Is this you, Psychic Stores? . . . Out of *business*? Why they were here a minute ago!

Pull Devil, Pull Beagle

A GOOD MANY YEARS AGO, about the time that "Perdicaris Alive or Raisuli Dead" was on everyone's tongue and I could quote Louise Glaum's bust measurement to the fraction of an inch, I conceived an idea for a play. Briefly, it was to deal with a group of people in a shabby boarding house, into whose midst would come a mysterious stranger with infinite compassion and a face illumined from within by a light not of this world. By the time the final curtain fell, this character (whom I clearly saw being played by H. B. Warner) would reconcile the lovers, rehabilitate a wanton, vindicate a suspected embezzler, restore crotchety old Miss Sprague's faith in humanity, and vanish without betraying his identity. Word of my project must have leaked out, because I had hardly procured several stout nibs and a packet of foolscap from the corner stationery store when *The Passing of the Third Floor Back* appeared and overnight I became a pariah.

It was a bitter draught, but I swallowed it. For a long time I lay fallow, and then another idea—this time for a novel—slowly took form in my mind. It would mirror the disillusion and moral bankruptcy of postwar English society, a subject with which I was intimately acquainted. I chose as heroine a woman of singular beauty, beauty that bade fair to destroy the men it attracted. I planned to make Orchid Marsh the symbol of decadent Mayfair—brittle, reckless, yet somehow as gallant and splendid as the hat she wore. The suicide of her husband as a gesture of purity, her feverish succession of affairs with cads and wastrels, her tragic self-destruction at the wheel of a high-powered roadster—innumerable details suggested themselves as I legged it to the stationery store. The clerk was just wrapping up my nibs and foolscap when I idly picked up a new novel called *The Green Hat*. . . . Well, I am the last to begrudge Michael Arlen his success. He merely got the story down on paper before I did. All the same, it's pretty rough when it happens twice in a lifetime. And when it happens a *third* time, you begin to get a thoughtful little line between the eyebrows.

The third time, specifically, was one night a few weeks

ago, when I picked up Sidney Skolsky's movie column and read the following: "Julie Haydon has sold a book containing just love letters to her dog. It will be published by Marcel Rodd." Now, it goes without saying that the love letters of a celebrated actress to her dog are a juicy plum in any publishing season and Mr. Rodd may be pardoned for smacking his lips. Ironically enough, however, one week before, I had concluded arrangements with Mr. Spencer Gouge of Fly-By-Night Editions to issue a volume of love letters written to me by a young beagle I bought this summer. The felicity of phrase, the emotional maturity which mark these letters would be arresting in a full-grown dog; in a six-months-old puppy, they are nothing short of extraordinary. Nevertheless, since a book by a famous personality like Miss Haydon must overshadow one by an obscure beagle, and since I have no desire to queer her pitch, I have decided to withdraw the dog's letters from publication. I submit only a few to convince possible skeptics of their authenticity and flavor. If they occasionally verge on the fulsome, it should be remembered that the dog was very much in love with me at the moment. I subsequently had occasion to kick him downstairs several times and his affection may have cooled somewhat.

SEPTEMBER 9

DEAR CHIEF,

What a privilege it is to live in the same house with someone like you. Whenever I hear people talking behind your back, saying things like "He's nursing the first nickel he ever made" and "Can you imagine seeing that phiz over a breakfast table?" it makes my blood boil. All right, so you *are* a bit stingy with your money. So you *do* trip over your feet when you walk. So your head *does* come to a point on top. Whose fault is that? You can't help those things any more than I can help having eleven champions in my pedigree and a blood line that goes back six hundred years.

Incidentally, since we're on the subject of ancestry, I happened to run across your family album while chewing up some of your books. Those relatives of yours certainly are a weird lot—all shapes and sizes. Some real dillies there, boy. Of course this heredity business is bunk and all that, but don't you think people would be a lot less critical of you if they could have a look at your genealogy? I mean to say, you don't expect to find a prize pippin in a barrel of rotten apples. Now, take my folks, on the other hand. My great-grandfather was best of breed three years running at Westminster—silver cups all over the place. He sired Saddlerock Nainsook Bravo, who belonged to the former lieutenant governor of West Virginia. With that kind of stock, you get real character. See the difference, old man?

Up to now, I've hesitated to broach the food situation to you, but you might as well know what's going on in your own household. Yesterday your wife chipped the rust off her change purse and bought me a pat of hamburger, just large enough to engrave the Lord's Prayer on. The minute she left the kitchen, the maid swallowed it. I gave her a good bite in the flank, but it didn't taste the same. I'm telling you, boss, I've had all the ersatz I intend to eat. If I don't get some protein pretty soon, you'd better watch those children of yours.

In fact, you'd better watch a lot of things, among them the people in the flat next door to you. Did you know that the lady who lives there came home the other evening and found her husband washing a couple of ghosts in the bathtub? There was a very penetrating smell of Coty perfume in the air, and she asked what he was doing. "Why, nothing, dear," he replied. "I'm just separating the chypre from the ghosts." Now, what do you make of that?

Yours devotedly,

FLASH

SEPTEMBER 27

DEAR CHIEF,

I'm no doctor, but I'll give you some friendly advice. That shade of purple you've taken to turning recently, every time anything unusual happens, has me worried. One minute you're your usual shark's-belly white, and the next, without any transition, you look like an eggplant. Better watch the old temper, Mac.

For instance, Tuesday night when you came home from the movies. O.K., somebody had short-circuited the lamps, eaten a hole in the sofa, and strewn kapok all over the floor.

It might have been anyone—that part-time peon of yours or those part-time chimpanzees masquerading as children. Had you asked me, I could have told you that your domestic lost three previous jobs because of her appetite for sofas. Instead, you chased me through the apartment, screaming the most bloodcurdling oaths and flailing around with a broom. Personally, I enjoyed the romp and slept beautifully afterward, even if you did puff like a donkey engine all night long. Don't play bean-bag with your arteries, brother, or you'll wind up in a rolling chair at French Lick.

Speaking of health, maybe you'd like to know what kind of starvation diet one member of the family unit is subsisting on. For dinner today, I was fed a moist mash containing these certified ingredients: soybean flour, wheat middlings, dried whey, yeast culture, manganese sulphate, oyster-shell flour, bone meal, and limestone. Some beano, eh? Nothing like limestone to stick to the ribs. To top it off, I come into the dining room and find you, with your napkin tucked in below your third chin, gorging yourself on pot roast, baked potato, buttered carrots, chocolate cake, and coffee. All it needed to complete the composition was a big platter and an apple in your mouth.

I can't figure out the Imbries, those neighbors on our floor. I overheard Mrs. Imbrie telling the elevator boy that they've got a drunken Balkan couple at their country place who are constantly smashing up this little army truck they use. One night last weekend, Imbrie heard a crash near the bar and ran out to investigate. After a while, his wife called from a bedroom window and asked what he was doing. "Why, nothing, dear," Imbrie called back. "I'm just separating the jeep from the Croats." Maybe you can make head or tail of it; it's beyond me.

Adoringly,
FLASH

OCTOBER 11

DEAR CHIEF,

Every time I've come into the room the past few days, there's been more intrigue and buzzing than backstage at the Russian ballet. Do you think I don't realize what those sickly smiles and sudden endearments signify? You've got it all fixed to get me out of the way; I know too much. Well, if that's the way you want to play it, go ahead. But before you hire a couple of mongrels to waylay me up a dark alley, or ship me off to the kennel, or whatever you're cooking up, you may as well know the score.

As you read this, the S.P.C.A. has in its safe a sealed envelope, to be opened within forty-eight hours after I disappear. It contains a highly illuminating graph analyzing the recurrence of pot roast, steak, and other luxury meats on your menu. It also contains a documented account of such starvation and maltreatment of a small animal as has rarely been compiled in our time. This communication could be so extremely embarrassing that I'm sure you'd prefer to sit down with me and work out a modus vivendi. . . . I always say "blackmail" is such an ugly word, don't you? Call it, rather, a gentleman's agreement.

For after all, that is what we both are—gentlemen. The mere fact that my kin have run with the Quorn pack for sixteen generations and yours still wear ready-made clothing is irrelevant; I refuse to judge a man by his atrocious table manners or his gaudy hand-me-downs. He may be a wife-beater, turncoat, sycophant, and moral beachcomber, but underneath, deep down, one can discern fugitive traces of decency. Perhaps, if there were enough top round in it for me, I could show him the road to salvation.

As for that Imbrie couple in the next apartment, I've frankly given up trying to comprehend their behavior. Last night they threw a big cocktail party jammed with Broadway celebrities, columnists, and what all. Halfway through it, a violent altercation started between a radical journalist and some lady correspondent named Alice Leone something or other—I didn't catch the last part. Imbrie finally had to step in and break it up, and his wife asked him what he was doing. "Why, nothing, dear," he assured her. "I'm just separating the creep from the Moats." Of course, I heard this through the wall and I may have missed a word or two.

Well, *hasta luego,* kiddo, and keep your nose clean. If I don't hear from you before, I'll see you in the breadline.

Eternally yours,

Flash

Sleepy-time Extra

When it was first noised along Publishers' Row that the John B. Pierce Foundation, a nonprofit research organization, had instituted a survey dealing with American family behavior, attitudes, and possessions, public opinion was instantly split into two camps—into the larger and drowsier of which I fell. There is nothing like a good, painstaking survey full of decimal points and guarded generalizations to put a glaze like a Sung vase on your eyeball. Even the fact that the results of the poll were to be printed in that most exciting of current periodicals, *Business Week*, did little to allay my fatigue. Then, one morning in early April, hell started popping at my corner stationery store. "What's good today, Clinton?" I asked, browsing over the magazine rack. "Well, I tell you," replied Clinton, thoughtfully scratching the stubble on his chin (he raised corn there last year but is letting it lie fallow this season), "we just got the new number of *Business Week* containing the John B. Pierce Foundation survey on American family behavior, attitudes, and possessions." "Well, dog my cats!" I exclaimed, struck all of a heap. "Let's have a nickel's worth of those licorice gumdrops, will you, Clinton?" "Sure," said Clinton reluctantly, "but how about this new number of *Business Week* containing the John B. Pierce Foundation—" "Listen, Clinton," I said suddenly, "did you hear a funny little click just then?" "Aha," breathed Clinton, round-eyed. "What was it?" "A customer closing his account," I snapped, closing my account and taking my custom elsewhere.

It took a stray copy of the Buffalo *Evening News*, abandoned late yesterday afternoon on my bus seat by some upstate transient, to reveal the true nature of the survey and dispel my apathy. "Married Couples Favor Double Beds," trumpeted the dispatch. "Eighty-seven per cent of husbands and wives sleep together in double beds but 5% of the wives are dissatisfied with this and 40% think maybe twin beds would be ideal, *Business Week* magazine reported today on the basis of a survey by the John B. Pierce Foundation, nonprofit research organization. Other conclusions of the survey . . . included: In summer, 70.3% of the wives sleep in nightgowns, 24% in pajamas, 5% in the nude, and seven-tenths of 1% in shorts. Sixteen per cent of the women reported they would like to sleep in the nude, causing the Pierce Foundation to comment: 'Here we have clear-cut evidence of an inhibition.' . . . Fifty per cent of the husbands report no activity after getting into bed, 22% read, 12% talk, 7% listen to the radio, 3% say their prayers, 4% smoke, 2% eat. Comparable percentages for wives were 40% no activity, 29% read, 11% talk, 8% listen to the radio, 5% say their prayers, 3% think, 2% smoke, 2% eat."

Though one could speculate on the foregoing until the cows came home and distill all manner of savory psychological inferences, I cannot help wondering what machinery the Foundation used to obtain its statistics. Even the most incurious student of the report, I think, must ask himself eventually whether these delicious confidences were stammered into a telephone mouthpiece, or haltingly penned in a questionnaire, or whispered to a clear-eyed, bedirndled Bennington girl at the kitchen door. Somehow there is a grim, authoritative quality about the project which convinces me that the researchers went right to the source for their data, and I venture to think that more than one must have found himself embroiled in a situation like the following:

[*Scene: The bedroom of the Stringfellows, a standard middle-aged couple. Monty Stringfellow is a large, noisy extro-*

vert who conceals his insecurity under a boisterous good humor. He affects heavy, hobnailed Scotch brogues and leather patches at the elbows of his sports jackets, is constantly roaring out songs commanding you to quaff the nut-brown ale, and interlards his speech with salty imprecations like "Gadzooks" and "By my halidom." Tanagra, his wife, is a sultry, discontented creature on whom fifteen years of life with a jolly good fellow have left their mark. As the curtain rises, Monty, in a tweed nightgown, is seated upright in their double bed singing a rollicking tune, to which he beats time with a pewter tankard and a churchwarden pipe. Tanagra, a sleep mask over her eyes, is trying to catch a little shut-eye and getting nowhere.]

MONTY (*con brio*):

"Come quaff the nut-brown ale, lads,
For youth is all too fleeting,
We're holding high wassail, lads,
And life's dull care unheeding,
So quaff the nut-brown ale, lads—"

TANAGRA: Oh, shut up, for God's sake! You and your nut-brown ale.

MONTY: What's wrong?

TANAGRA: Nothing. Nothing at all. What makes you think anything's wrong?

MONTY: I don't know—you seem to be on edge lately. Every time I open my mouth, you snap my head off.

TANAGRA: Every time you open your mouth, that blasted tune comes out. Haven't you anything else in your song bag?

MONTY: Gee, Tanagra, I always looked on it as our theme song, you might say. (*Sentimentally*) Don't you remember that first night at the Union Oyster House in Boston, when you made me sing it over and over?

TANAGRA: You swept me off my feet. I was just a silly little junior at Radcliffe.

MONTY: You—you mean our moment of enchantment has passed?

TANAGRA: I'll go further. Many's the night I've lain here awake studying your fat neck and praying for a bow string to tighten around it.

MONTY (*resentfully*): That's a heck of a thing to say. You keep up that kind of talk and pretty soon we'll be sleeping in twin beds.

TANAGRA: O. K. by me, chum.

VOICE (*under bed*): Aha!

MONTY: What's that? Who said that?

TANAGRA: I'm sure I don't know.

MONTY: There's somebody under this bed!

VOICE: There's nobody here except just us researchers from the John B. Pierce Foundation.

MONTY: W-what are you doing down there?

VOICE: Conducting a survey. (*Otis "Speedball" Ismay, ace statistician of the Foundation, a personable young executive, crawls into view from under the Stringfellow four-*

poster, flips open his notebook.) Evening, friends. Close, isn't it?

TANAGRA (*archly*): I never realized how close.

ISMAY: You the lady of the house? I'd like to ask a few questions.

MONTY: Now just a minute. I don't know whether I approve—

TANAGRA: Batten down, stupid, he's not talking to you. (*Brightly*) Yes?

ISMAY: Let me see. You prefer sleeping in a nightgown rather than pajamas?

TANAGRA: Well, that depends. With this clod, a girl might as well wear a burlap bag.

ISMAY (*with a disparaging glance*): Yeah, strictly from Dixie. You know, that's a darned attractive nightie you've got on right now.

TANAGRA: What, *this* old thing?

ISMAY: It sends *me,* and I'm a tough customer. What do they call these doodads along the top?

TANAGRA: Alençon lace.

ISMAY: Cunning, aren't they?

TANAGRA (*provocatively*): Think so?

ISMAY (*tickling her*): Ootsie-kootsie!

TANAGRA: Now you stop, you bad boy.

MONTY: Hey, this is a pretty peculiar survey, if you ask me.

TANAGRA: Nobody asked you.

ISMAY: Wait a second. You *could* tell me one thing, Mister—Mister—

MONTY: Stringfellow. Monty Stringfellow.

ISMAY: Do you belong to any lodges, fraternal associations, or secret societies?

MONTY: What kind do you mean?

ISMAY (*impatiently*): It doesn't matter. Any kind that keeps you busy evenings.

MONTY: Why, yes. I'm Past Grand Chalice of the Golden Cupbearers of the World, field secretary of the Rice Institute Alumni—

ISMAY: Fine, fine. Don't bother to list them. We merely wish to know what evenings you spend away from home.

MONTY: Every Tuesday and every other Friday. Is this all part of the survey?

ISMAY: Part? It's practically the lifeblood. Well, I think you've given me all the information I need. Oh, just one more detail, Mrs. Stringfellow. You understand there's a high percentage of error in an informal cross-section of this type and naturally we like to check our findings.

TANAGRA: Naturally.

ISMAY: I'd ask you to drop in at my office, but it's being redecorated.

TANAGRA: Yes, I read something in the paper to that effect. Is it serious?

ISMAY: No, no, it'll be all right in a day or two. For the time being, I've moved my charts and figures to the Weylin

Bar, third table on the left as you come in at four-fifteen tomorrow afternoon.

TANAGRA: I'll be there half an hour early.

ISMAY: Splendid. (*To Stringfellow*) Thanks, old man, don't bother to show me to the door; I'll use the fire escape. Couple more calls to make in the building. Good night, all! (*He goes.*)

MONTY (*chortling*): Ho ho, that bird certainly pulled the wool over your eyes! He's no statistician. He didn't even have a fountain pen!

TANAGRA (*placidly*): Well, I swan. He sure took me in.

MONTY: Yes siree bob, you've got to get up pretty early in the morning to fool old Monty Stringfellow! (*He slaps her thigh familiarly and Tanagra sets her alarm for six forty-five.*)

CURTAIN

Amo, Amas, Amat, Amamus, Amatis, Enough

Yesterday morning I awoke in a pool of glorious golden sunshine laced with cracker crumbs to discover that spring had returned to Washington Square. A pair of pigeons were cooing gently directly beneath my window; two squirrels plighted their troth in a branch overhead; at the corner a handsome member of New York's finest twirled his night-stick and cast roguish glances at the saucy-eyed flower vendor. The scene could have been staged only by a Lubitsch; in fact, Lubitsch himself was seated on a bench across the street, smoking a cucumber and looking as cool as a cigar.

It lacked only Nelson Eddy to appear on a penthouse terrace and loose a chorus of deep-throated song, and, as if by magic, Nelson Eddy suddenly appeared on a penthouse terrace and, with the artistry that has made his name a word, launched into an aria. A moment later, Jeanette MacDonald, in creamy negligee, joined the dashing rascal, making sixty-four teeth, and the lovers began a lilting duet. The passers-by immediately took up the refrain; windows flew up at the Brevoort, flew down again; the melody spread rapidly up Fifth Avenue, debouched into Broadway, detoured into Park, and soon the entire city was humming the infectious strain in joyous tribute to Jeanette's and Nelson's happiness.

Caught up in the mood of the moment, I donned a jaunty foulard bow, stuck a feather in my hatband and one in my throat, and set out to look over spring fashions in love. That I ultimately wound up with a slight puff under one eye and a warning from a policewoman is not germane to the discussion. Truth is a wood violet that blooms in the least likely corner, and I found it in a couple of obscure pulp magazines called *Gay Love Stories* and *Ideal Love*, which retail at a dime apiece. Twenty cents for a postgraduate course in passion— *entre nous*, kids, I think I've got the only game in town.

Biologically, it was reassuring to find that the war had wrought no intrinsic change in the characters who people cut-rate romantic fiction; the smooth and deadly function of the glands continues undisturbed by the roar of high explosives. The ladies are as cuddly and adorable as they were before Pearl Harbor, the cavaliers as manly and chivalrous as any immortalized by Nell Brinkley and Leyendecker. Consider, for instance, Linda Marshall, the colleen of "Little Ball of Catnip," in the May *Ideal Love,* as she stands lost in dreams in her garden at Santa Monica, "slender and poised in a brown and white seersucker dress, the tight bodice cunningly trimmed in rickrack braid. She had a clear skin, nicely accented by dark eyebrows, lively hazel eyes, and beautifully fashioned cherry-red lips. The general impression was that of youth on the wing." Incidentally, there seems to be a strange, almost Freudian compulsion in both magazines to describe the heroine in avian terms—*vide* Kitty Malcolm in "Barefoot Blonde" (*Gay Love*): "That evening, after finishing a careful toilette, Kitty glanced at herself in the mirror, and knew that she had never looked lovelier. The black velvet gown molded her slim figure to perfection. In the gleaming nest of curls which she had scooped atop her head, Steve's gardenias, which had arrived via messenger, provided the last, elegant touch." It seems almost picayune of Steve not to have included a clutch of cold-storage eggs in the nest atop his inamorata's head as an earnest of eventual domesticity.

An even more tempting *bonne bouche* than Kitty is Bonita Kellsinger, grooming her lovely frame for the evening in "Shadow of Her Past" (*Gay Love,* June): "The very thought of such a triumph [winning the richest boy in Barnesville] brought roses to her richly tanned cheeks, brought a fiery sparkle into her wide, greenish-blue eyes. She brushed her thick, ripe-wheat colored hair until it hung on her straight slender shoulders in rich gleaming waves. A pair of small jewelled clips held back one wave of hair on either side of the girl's high, intelligent forehead. She made an enticing red rosebud of her mouth, and wound ropes of scarlet wooden beads around her neck and arms." Small wonder indeed that her gallant fidgets impatiently off scene at the wheel of his station wagon, which the author introduces parenthetically in one of the most syncopated bits of whitewash on record: "Cary had explained that he couldn't get adequate rations of gas for any of his cars but the wagon, which he used in working hours to haul people to and from his canning factory that was so busy putting up dehydrated foods for the Army and Navy." For sheer pith, the passage deserves a niche in the Hall of Ungainly Exposition beside my all-time favorite, which graced one of the early Fu Manchu films. Briefly, the artful Doctor had eluded Nayland Smith by swarming down a rope ladder into the Thames. The ensuing scene revealed a vast underground cavern, in the foreground a rough deal table piled high with crucibles, alembics, and retorts bubbling with sinister compounds. After a pause, the table swung away, a trapdoor opened, and Dr. Fu crept up, followed by a henchman (Tully Marshall). "Well, Wing Chang," remarked the Doctor with a fiendish chuckle, "these old dye works certainly make an admirable laboratory of crime, do they not?"

Since every one of the nineteen novelettes and short stories I dipped into was written by a woman, the result is a gallery of fairly glamorous males, nearly all of them named Michael. It is practically six, two, and even that at some point in the action tiny muscles are going to flicker in lean jaws, eyes crinkle up quizzically at the corners, and six feet of lanky, bronzed strength strain a reluctant miss against a rough khaki shoulder (apparently the supply of smooth khaki shoulders has been exhausted, for whatever reason). There must have been a singularly dreamy look in the eye of Betty Webb Lucas, the author of "Blue Angel" (*Gay Love*), when she hatched Dr. Michael Halliday, chief surgeon of the City Hospital: "He was more like a Greek god, in spite of the flaming hair that threatened to break into rebellious curls at any moment, and the sterile white jacket straining over broad shoulders. His eyes were incredibly blue, and his sun-bronzed skin made them seem bluer still." Much as I respect honest emotion, I am afraid Miss Lucas became a trifle too dreamy in her medical dialogue: "Judy could only stare until he said impatiently: 'Haven't you anything else to do but stand there peering at me like a—a biological specie?' " The most charitable assumption in defense of Miss Lucas must be that the dear nearness of Judy in her crisp white nurse's uniform unnerved the eminent man.

It is hardly surprising that when these golden lads and lasses finally have at one another, they produce an effect akin to the interior of a blast furnace. Observe the Wagnerian encounter between the aforementioned Bonita Kellsinger and her beau ideal: "He caught her close to him, pinned her cheek against the rough khaki shoulder of his uniform, and slowly, deliberately covered her mouth with his, in a kiss that made her forget everything for the moment in the heady rapture of it. . . . They seemed to ascend to the top of a very high mountain, where there hung a white disc of moon in a sparkling bed of stars, and a soft breeze scented with jasmine swept over them. But when his lips lifted from hers, it was as though the cables had been cut from an elevator. She hit earth with a bump that shocked her awake." While Bonita brushes the meteorites from her hair and recovers her land legs, take a hinge at Lieutenant Lex McClure flinging a bit of woo in "Glass Walls Are Cold" (*Ideal*): "Sally fought against it, but she felt as though she would die of the ecstasy that poured through her body. All of her senses quickened and became alert. She smelled the piney fragrance of his tobacco [that mixture of sun-dried burley and evergreen cones so popular of late with the armed forces] and the light scent of her own perfume. Her lips softened under his pressure, then she drew away softly, drawing her cheek across his chin, feeling the roughness of his day-old beard." Luckily, as one weaned on *The Perfumed Garden* and the Mardrus translation of *The Arabian Nights,* I was able to withstand this erotic play. Even so, I must confess that a bestial flush invaded my cheek and I had to fight off an overmastering impulse to pinch the hired girl.

At the risk of slighting any individual author, I must say the brightest star in the galaxy is unquestionably Leonora McPheeters whose "Perfumed Slacker" (*Ideal,* May) is subheaded "How could you love a man who always smelled like a boudoir?" For timeliness, melodrama, and a good old-fashioned concupiscence like Mother used to make, I haven't met its equal since the *Decameron.* The principals in this droll tale are two: John Craig, "tall, masculine, tweedy . . . a big overgrown Newfoundland pup, with his rough tawny hair and steady brown eyes," and Judy, a *zäftick* little proposition bent on bringing him to heel. Ostensibly the pair are engaged in running a cosmetic laboratory; actually, they seem to spend the business day mousing around each other, trading molten kisses, and generally overheating themselves. Occasionally Judy varies the routine by kissing Bob, a shadowy member in a soldier suit who drifts in from an unspecified reservation, but these ersatz embraces only sharpen her appetite for the brand of judo dispensed by Craig. Unfortunately, the intra-office romance withers when Judy detects her employer's lack of enthusiasm for military service, and excoriating him for a coward and a caitiff, she gives him the mitten. Then, in a whirlwind denouement, she captures two enemy agents by upsetting a carboy of wave set over their heads and learns to her stupefaction that Craig has really been evolving explosives for the government. As the curtain descends, Philemon seizes Baucis in a sizzling hammer lock, superbly indifferent to the fact that they are standing ankle-deep in thermite and TNT, and rains kisses on her upturned face.

By one of those coincidences that are positively spooky, the hired girl opened my door at this juncture and found the boss-man ankle-deep in a roomful of shredded pulp fiction, baying like a timber wolf. Before she could turn to flee, five feet seven of lanky, bronzed strength reached out and strained her against a rough pajama shoulder. I'm still trying to explain things to the employment agency, but they keep hanging up on me. You don't know anybody with full-fashioned cherry-red lips and a high, intelligent forehead who could help me with the housework, do you? She needn't bother about a uniform; just tell her to meet me in the Lombardy Bar at five tomorrow. They've got the best Dutch Cleanser in town.

Ms. Found in a Bottle of Firewater

GOD KNOWS I don't want to bring the whole medical fraternity down around my ears, but every time during the past five weeks I have tried to get the American Medical Association on the phone, all I got was a busy signal. Busy signal—what the hell are *they* busy about? Here is a man with possibly the most revolutionary discovery in medicine in forty years—a complete and lasting cure for alcoholism effective in ten minutes, without any drugs, plasters, or leeches, and guaranteed to leave the sufferer free of any craving—and what do I get? A busy signal.

And mind you, this isn't one of those theoretical things—I've tried it myself. Frankly, boys, I used to be a perfect monster in my cups; beat the wife, drank away her dowry, beat the children, drank away *their* dowry—a textbook case. Now I can take the stuff or leave it alone. Nine or ten Martinis before dinner, half a dozen highballs, and a few brandy-and-sodas at bedtime are all I care for, thank you. But it's the other fellow I'm thinking of, the poor wretch who doesn't know when to quit. That's who I'm thinking of.

Oddly enough, I encountered the cure completely by accident. I hadn't intended to go on the wagon at all—quite the reverse. I was tooling my stylish Velie Six through the mountain passes of New Mexico last spring when darkness overtook me about seventy miles from Gallup. For a moment I played with the thought of spending the night on a mesa and dining on boiled tumbleweed, but Gallup proved irresistible and I put the accelerator down to the floor. I regret to say it stayed there, and what is more, so did I. I made my entrance into Gallup five hours later in somewhat ignominious fashion, rather high up in the air and facing backward from the tow-car. Not a muscle flickered in my lean jaw, however, as our little procession moved past the group of cattlemen lounging outside the Golden Girl Saloon, and their pithy comments had long since died away before I permitted myself a muttered "Swine." There is nothing like a muttered "Swine" to pick you up after such an ordeal unless it is a stiff drink, and I promptly went in search of same.

I soon discovered time had wrought one major change in Gallup since my last visit. The principal hotel now boasted a cocktail room which had sprung full-blown from the forehead of A. A. Milne. It bore the poetic name of "The Lodge of the Four Smokes" and it was underground—a detail which immediately gave me a slightly entombed feeling and set me breathing through my gills like a carp. The décor consisted of corn husks and a sand floor illuminated by two or three orange bulbs. I do not look well underground, and orange bulbs do nothing to counteract the condition. But it was not until the pretty hostess in flowing green pajamas placed the wine list in front of me that I realized I was a gone goose.

The wet goods sold in "The Lodge of the Four Smokes" were divided into several categories as antic as anything you would encounter in a day's hard writhing. Under the heading of "Big Medicine" were assembled cocktails, punches, and fizzes with such vibrant names as "The Flight of the Eagle" (planter's punch), "The War God's Rickey" (sloe gin fizz), and "Rain Cloud Julep" (hot buttered rum punch). "Snake Bite Medicine," of course, embraced the whiskies, while "Bitter Root Medicine" included brews with such lovely old Indian tribal names as Blatz and Schlitz. Wines, both still and sparkling, were listed under the general classification of "The Earth Mother's Medicine" ("She Who Changes"), and the liqueurs as "Son of the Sun's Medicine" ("He Who Kills Fear"). Oddly enough, a special department entitled "Frog's Medicine" offered Apollinaris, Poland Water, and kindred beverages to any frog who might wander in, though I would have supposed from its location that the bar catered chiefly to moles and angleworms. For a moment I debated ordering a Ladder to Heaven cocktail (Bronx) on the chance that however rickety, it might at least get me up to the lobby floor, but the old reliable Two Moon cocktail (Martini) won out, and braiding a turkey feather into my topknot, I settled down to further study of the wine list.

I had engulfed approximately six moons and was watching my hands creeping about the tabletop for all the world like a couple of horseshoe crabs when a loud altercation broke out at the bar. Two patrons dressed in the fashion of Gene Autry, one of them unmistakably a Greek restaurateur from his accent and the other a Navajo, were squaring off at each other menacingly. "Don' brandy your fish at me!" the Navajo was shouting. "Go on, you greaser!" snarled the Greek, "I'll teach you the code of the West!" Before I could discover what canon of the code had been violated, the Greek caught up his half-emptied glass and flung it at his friend. It exploded against a pillar roughly six inches from my head, or rather from where my head had been resting, for I was already rushing it upstairs to apply cold compresses to it. The next time you're in "The Lodge of the Four Smokes," just ask the hostess about the paleface with the glasses who suddenly got claustrophobia. I believe they still call me "Bad Medicine" (He Who Cops a Sneak Without Paying the Tab).

Whatever Goes Up

WHEN IT WAS ANNOUNCED a few days ago in *Variety* that a new musical comedy named *What's Up?* dealing with the misadventures of some aviators whose plane is grounded near a girls' school, was cooling on top of the oven, Broadway's reaction was not slow in coming. "That's for me," observed one astute old showman with whom I was lunching at Lindy's. "I'll take a piece of that." The moment the waiter had brought him the strudel, however, he seemed less certain. "I don't know," he hesitated, trying to ingest the strudel without removing his toothpick and cigar. "It's a kind of a sophisticated idea. The public don't want to think—they want to laugh. Look at Chekhov." We looked at Chekhov, who had just come in and was having a rolled-beef sandwich and a bottle of Dr. Brown's Celery Tonic in the corner. I got up and went over to his table.

"Hello, Chekhov," I said.

"Hello," he said.

"What happened to *you* last night?" I said.

"Brett and I waited for you at the Dingo," he said. Good old Chekhov. I could see him looking at the *Variety* in my pocket.

"Well, I guess you know," I said.

"Sure," he said. "Sure. I know."

"I suppose it had to happen," I said.

"Not that way it didn't," he said. "Not that way, old man. When I wrote *Uncle Vanya* none of *my* aviators were grounded near a girls' school."

"You didn't have any aviators in *Uncle Vanya,*" I said.

"You bet I didn't," he said. "That's the point." He ordered another Celery Tonic.

"Better ease off, Chekhov," I said. "That makes four."

"I'm all right," he said cheerfully. That's one thing about Chekhov. No matter how many Dr. Browns he's had, he never shows it. "Mind if I file some cables?" He drew some cables from his pocket and started filing them. I went back to my table and told my friend what he had said.

"Certainly," he nodded. "It ain't believable, aviators mixed up in a girls' school. Listen," he said confidentially, impaling a sour tomato on his index finger, "do you want to know what an astute old showman like I would do with that plot? I'd make them a bunch of girl aviators which they fall down near a boys' school. Paste that in your hat and smoke it."

I have been smoking it ever since last Tuesday and have arrived at the same conclusion. The basic idea of *What's Up?* is a dilly, but unless it is handled with extreme delicacy it may very well curdle. In the following libretto, I have taken the liberty of indicating one of the directions in which the story might go. There is still another, but I doubt whether the authors could be influenced to accept it at this point.

[*Scene 1: The cockpit of a fast monoplane high above the clouds. At rise, three fair aeronauts are discovered in white sateen uniforms with cute fur-trimmed collars and goggles: Phyllis Brontislaw, a gorgeous blonde; Valuta Imbrie, a gorgeous brunette; and Punkins Janeway, a gorgeous red-head. Valuta has just finished washing her luxuriant tresses and, while Phyllis busies herself steering their frail craft, spreads her crowning glory out to dry in the rays of the late-afternoon sun. Punkins, curled up on a sofa, is gorging herself on Tango Kisses and devouring the latest Donn Byrne novel.*]

VALUTA: Well, here we are in the trackless empyrean, where every prospect pleases and only man is vile.

PHYLLIS: Men, men, men—can't you think of anything else?

PHYLLIS (*solo*):
"Men, Men, Men"

Oh, maidens fair, beware,
And likewise have a care,
Lest passion's kiss betrays
And lose you in a maze.

Men, men, men,
They're quite outside our ken,
Their ways are very devious,
It's lovey-us and leavey-us,
Men, men, men.

PUNKINS: Why so pensive, Val?

VALUTA: That's for me to know and you to find out.

PHYLLIS: Stuff and double stuff! All the world is aware that your aunt, Mrs. Morris Fenchurch of Shaker Heights and Piping Rock, made me take you along on my transcontinental dash to nip your budding romance with Señor Ramón Mulcahy, the Argentinian polo flash that has been turning feminine heads this season!

VALUTA (*hotly*): I'll have you know I'm in love with Ramón and propose to marry him!

PHYLLIS: We shall see what we shall see.

PUNKINS: Oh, stop scrapping, you two! Say, Phyl, what time are we due in Bethesda, Maryland?

PHYLLIS: Unless my eyes are playing me false, I believe I descry her environs now. *Oh!*

PUNKINS: What's the matter?

PHYLLIS: The engine's missing!

PUNKINS (*innocently*): Then how did we ever get this far?

PHYLLIS (*impatiently*): Something has gone wrong with the mechanism, silly. (*Thoughtfully*) Doubtless one of those little wheels inside is stuck.

VALUTA: Then it behooves us to "bail off" apace, lest we dash out our brains in the ensuing holocaust. Parachutes at the ready! (*Galvanized into action, the three pull their rip-cords and float gently to earth. Midway they are joined by the ladies of the ensemble, forming a stunning aerial ballet which should leave the critics breathless in their seats. Note: This may be a bit difficult to stage, as the plane is resting on two sawhorses and the parachutes are bound to create hell's own tangle, but it can all be cut out on the road.*)

[*Scene 2: A dormitory room at Peachpit Military Academy. At rise, Perry Yeast, president of the senior class, is stretched disconsolately on a window seat, staring at the ceiling. His adoring henchman, "Skinny" Beaumarchais, whose bulk belies his sobriquet, surveys him with a look of anxiety on his rubicund physiognomy.*]

PERRY: Well, here we are on the eve of the annual Senior

Hop and every girl at Miss Breitigam's sequestered with botulism resulting from substandard tinned meats. What to do?

SKINNY (*struck by an inspiration*): I've got it, Chief! Why not charter a speedboat and run down to Montevideo, fabled for its feminine pulchritude?

SKINNY (*comic rumba*):

We'll throw a party with the señoritas lively,
There'll be rum and gourds and castanets, so drive me
To that cluster of palmettos and cabañas,
Where the mangoes are so fine, and the bananas. Etc.

PERRY: That's all very well, but the dance is scheduled to begin in half an hour, and if crusty Dean Vogelsang discovers we have no girls he will call it off, thereby making us a laughing stock.

SKINNY: It looks like we're sunk, unless some girls drop out of the sky. (*A knock at the door; enter Phyllis, Valuta, and Punkins, scantily clad.*)

PHYLLIS: Quick—hide us!

PERRY (*curiously*): What's the matter?

PHYLLIS: Crotchety, near-sighted Dean Vogelsang's suspicions are aroused! There he is on the staircase now!

PERRY: What's your name?

PHYLLIS: Phyllis Brontislaw.

PERRY: That's the most beautiful name I've ever heard.

PERRY *and* PHYLLIS (*duet*):

A man and a maid were strolling
In some grass that was covered with dew,
When he took her hand and boldly pledged,
"I'll e'er remember you.
Come place your ruby lips on mine,
And love is all too fleeting,
We're here where journeys always end,
I.e., in lovers' meeting."

[*Skinny hastily pushes the girls into a closet; enter Dean Vogelsang.*]

DEAN (*sternly*): Did I see three chickens run in here a minute ago?

PERRY: No, and you're a near-sighted old fossil.

DEAN (*adjusting his ear trumpet*): What's that? What's that?

PERRY: I said you sing as sweet as a throstle.

DEAN (*placated*): Well, that's different. Now mind you, Yeast, you have ten minutes to find partners for the Senior Hop or it's off.

PERRY (*deliberately*): I think . . . I may have . . . a surprise for you, Dean Vogelsang.

[*Scene 3: The school auditorium, that evening. Gay lanterns have transformed it into a veritable fairyland, and a three-piece combination consisting of Zinkeiser* (*piano*), *Hilde-*

brand (drums), and Suppositorsky (alto sax) is dispensing torrid rhythm. As laughing couples swirl by in the background, Skinny enters to the punchbowl at right, attended by his faithful henchman, "Happy" Telekian, whose mournful visage gainsays his nickname.]

HAPPY: Well, everybody is having loads of fun tonight, thanks to Perry's resourcefulness, but what are you putting in the punchbowl, Skinny?

SKINNY: Don't you catch on, stupid? It's our only chance. If Dean Vogelsang gets tipsy, he may not decide to flunk Perry in his forthcoming histology quiz, thus enabling us to beat Meatcliff and win the track crown at the conference.

HAPPY (*tensely*): We've only minutes to spare! (*The starter's pistol is heard off scene and the Meatcliff relay team flashes by on a treadmill at rear, a lap ahead of Peachpit. The crowd groans. Enter Punkins on Dean Vogelsang's arm.*)

PUNKINS (*flirtatiously*): Why, Vogie, you're a wonderful dancer—a regular Fred Astaire!

DEAN (*suspiciously*): What did you say about a chair?

PUNKINS: I said you were afraid to take a dare.

DEAN: Well, that's different. (*He drains a cup of punch, stifles a hiccough.*) Shay, girlie—hic—lesh you and I dansh.

PUNKINS (*craftily*): Will you let Perry run against Meatcliff? (*The crowd trembles on his decision.*)

DEAN: Yesh. (*He collapses in a drunken coma. As Perry doffs his "tux" and darts after the Meatcliff aggregation, the crowd goes wild with joy.*)

PHYLLIS: He's gaining!

VALUTA: Now he's at the turn! Now he's coming down the stretch! (*With a Herculean effort, Perry breasts the tape and the rooters execute a frenzied snake dance to "Peachpit, Mother of Men."*)

VALUTA (*nestling shyly in Perry's arms*): Well, thank goodness I got shut of that greaser Ramón in time to marry a clean-limbed American boy.

SKINNY (*to Mrs. Vetlugin, the house mother, who is extremely stout*): Well, I guess that's telling 'em, eh, fat lady? [*As Skinny and Happy pair off with Punkins and Valuta, the ensemble goes into a whirlwind finish, George Abbott goes into a passion, and the producers go into bankruptcy.*]

CURTAIN

Scrub Me, Mammy, Eight to the Bar

I WAS TURNING over a pile of back numbers of *Harper's Bazaar* this morning, using a pitchfork and taking care to keep them well away from the root system of the plants, when, on page 83 of the May issue, I suddenly encountered a naked young person presenting her saucy derrière to me. God's handiwork is ever sacred to me, and I should still be leaning on the handle of my fork and studying it had I not discovered it was simply window dressing for some text at the left. I hate to be disloyal to Miss Derrière but, juicy piece though she was, the piece she illustrated—Elinor Guthrie Neff's "How to Take a Bath"—was juicier.

"How to Take a Bath" is a canvass made by the *Bazaar* of seven distinguished ladies—Maureen Orcutt, Ina Claire, Dorothy Draper, Cornelia Otis Skinner, Lillian Hellman, Carol Bruce, and Dorothy Kilgallen—to elicit their bathing secrets. Exactly what motivated this important sociological survey is none too clear, but there seems to be a tacit implication that if milady adopts any of these various styles of bathing, she should be able to play top-flight golf, become an expert *farceur,* sing like an oriole, and girdle the globe. In my mind's eye I see Carmel Snow, the editor of the magazine, pacing her office and evolving the idea, her lovely brows contracted in thought. It is the typical office of the editor of a smart fashion journal—Victor Mature in white jodhpurs, a prominent analyst seated in a corner unravelling an old psyche, a willowy couturier making epigrams about high colonics. The mighty roar of the presses blends with the shrill cries of newsboys hawking the latest issue—"Wuxtry! Molyneux forecasts crêpe shantung with ballibuntl straw sailors! Read all about it!" With an abrupt gesture, Mrs. Snow removes her battered corncob (not a pipe, just an old corncob she chews to aid concentration) and barks a crisp command into the Dictograph. Seven tall, cool Vassar graduates enter and man their notebooks. A gasp of admiration echoes from the septet as the plan comes alive in words as deft and vivid as the pigments of an old master.

"And remember, you mugs," the editor snaps, "we're not running a fiction magazine. Bring me facts—the more intimate the better. Little human-interest touches—sponges, washcloths, anything you can lay your hands on. A bonus to the first one who comes up with a Turkish towel. That's all. Now *get*."

And they got, all right. From Maureen Orcutt, the noted golfer, they got the trembling-lipped confession that she is miserable under a cold shower. (That makes two of us who are miserable under a cold shower, honey.) Miss Orcutt has therefore evolved a striking way out: her showers are *warm*. Simple enough after it's explained, isn't it? But it took the kind of determination and tenacity that makes champions. There are more tricks up this lady's sleeve, however, than plain warm showers. "When her body is achy from fatigue," the *Bazaar* continues breathlessly, "she soaks in a hot tub, as you would in a steam room, not to cleanse but to relax. She uses bath salts, then. But desultorily, capriciously." Well, if you think Maureen Orcutt is desultory and capricious with her bath salts, you ought to see *me*. Why, one day I won't use more than the teentsy-weentsiest pinch, hardly a smidgen; the next, I'm liable to call for two or three hundred pounds. I know it's just crazy, but what are you going to *do?* It's the way I'm made. As I said to the wife the other night, "I suppose you'd like it better if I was some stodgy corn chandler in Hasbrouck Heights." Boy, did that shut her up!

Both Ina Claire and Dorothy Draper, one discovers, are given to sluicing their frames with great quantities of oil. "Cornelia Otis Skinner also uses oil in her bath—perhaps a hangover from a trick she had as a child," we are told. "She would oil the inside of the tub, sit on the rim, and whoop it all the way down to the other end, slithering at great speed along the bottom." I like to think of the noted actor whose name she bears trying to shave while Cornelia caromed about the bathroom, smashing bottles and denting the fixtures. I also like to think of the hired girl whose job it was to clean the tub every day. "Ish ka bibble," she must have muttered in her comical Irish and Ukrainian dialect. "What's the diff so long as she grows up to be an eminent mime?"

To portray the bath life of a playwright, which would appear to be a matter of purely polite interest even to a loyal member of the Dramatists' Guild, the *Bazaar* graciously condescends to the argot of Winchell: "Playwright Lillian Hellman takes baths that are much too piping hot and jumps in and out of them in a flash with a flash." Possibly this is intended to mean that the petite dramatist clenches an electric torch as she plummets in and out of her tub, but that would be sheer bohemianism in one so chic. The difference between author and actor is sharply illustrated in the final simonizing Miss Hellman and Carol Bruce give their respective chassis. Whereas Miss Hellman covers herself with a cloud of talcum, Miss Bruce uses ordinary cornstarch powder. It is only God's mercy that prevented the customers at *Louisiana Purchase* from having witnessed a horrid Jekyll-and-Hyde transformation right on stage and finding a pudding where they bargained for a songstress. A very cute dish, no doubt, but hardly worth three-thirty to a housewife who can duplicate it in her kitchen for a dime.

After all the frenzied energy and high-octane glamour of her fellows, Dorothy Kilgallen's crabbed disillusion comes as a welcome relief. "She won't go near a shower, not even on sweltering summer days," says the *Bazaar* with a superior smirk, "and even her husband who is eloquent on the soothing effects of a nice cooling shower can't persuade her. . . . She won't use crystals because she always forgets to put them in when she runs her bath, and then objects to sitting on them before they have time to melt. . . . She uses dusting powder except when she is going to wear dark clothes, and then she doesn't know how to cope with it." Miss Kilgallen is the colleen for me, alannah. If she doesn't mind a proposition from a complete stranger, I know a Russian bath down on Grand Street where they never heard of skin-softeners, English bath mitts, and pine oil. For fifty cents you get a locker and a corned-beef sandwich and a key to wear around your neck. Mind you, you don't necessarily have to wear the locker and the corned-beef sandwich around your neck, but all the really smart people are doing it. And that's the kind of inside dope you'll *never* get from *Harper's Bazaar.*

Whiskey Rebellion

THOUGH HARDLY in the sere and yellow leaf, I still get a moderate boot out of the thought that what is called "modern advertising" (for want of a better name, such as, for instance, Smitty or Alice J. Fabricant) was born and attained its fine flower in my time. So apart from a little pleasant masochism, there is no point in dwelling on such memories as that photograph of a young lady, eyeballs rolling orgiastically, clutching an automobile radiator to her frame; the débutante gnawing wolfishly on a turkey leg in the interests of Pepsodent; the depilatory advertisements with their honeyed catch phrases; and the whole torrent of coaxing, admonition, and execration directed at the erogenous zones. Even after twenty-five years spent training myself to read cautiously, I occasionally catch glimpses of smirking housewives fingering each other's lace curtains and whispering, "Tattletale gray, my dear." Such dark humors as those catalogued by *Printer's Ink*—Acid Blues, Bird-cage Mouth, Bridge-table Slump, Floor Pox, Headline Jitters, Lobsteritis, Prairie Squint, Radiosis, Transportation Fatigue, Vacation Figure, and Five O'Clock Shadow—are only a few of the ailments charted for us by the advertising agencies. Stopping in Los Angeles a while ago, I was thrown back on a Sunday newspaper whose comic supplement was largely taken up with the adventures of a boy, his skin, and some yeast tablets. Brother, you don't *know*.

For whatever reason, possibly because they were subjected to fourteen years of hibernation, the whiskey advertisements in particular have been outvying each other to jog the imagination and fray the nerves. Talk about Pavlov's dogs! Thanks to the series sponsored by Dewar & Son, the casual drinker has been so thoroughly conditioned by now that he would rather die of thirst than take a dram without the proper busby. It is no longer permissible to whip into the corner shebeen for a quick jolt dressed in dungarees or a heavy rope-knit sweater; you are now a clodhopper indeed unless you clank around in the full regimentals of the Argyll and Sutherland Highlanders or the Dublin Fusiliers. If I can't recite every skirmish from Inkerman to the Plains of Abraham, it is certainly not the fault of the distillers. The assumption seems to be that whatever Scotch the Lancers drank before engaging the Fuzzy-Wuzzies is good enough for me as I advance on my butcher to alibi last month's bill. Mr. Schaefer has enough on me already without my swaggering in with a horsehair plume and spitting a sirloin with my claymore.

Nor have the purveyors of such homely brews as rye and bourbon been dozing, either. For years, when the occasion demanded, one felt free to down a couple of fingers of rye whether dressed in pajamas or a smoking jacket, but that time is past. Today I am a whimpering thrall of Schenley Distributors, Inc., and maintain at considerable expense a rough shooting coat, an under-and-over shotgun, and a brace of golden retrievers whom I detest. And just try to sneak a *vermouth-cassis* past those liquid brown eyes if you want to break your heart, to say nothing of incurring a nasty bite in the foot. Until recently I was prevented from drinking bourbon not by any physiological barrier or lack of means (I happen to be extremely wealthy; my grandfather was a dishonest sutler in the Army of the Tennessee), but because I had neglected to provide myself with a frock coat, a frilled shirt, and a white imperial. Latterly I have put in three mornings a week teetering on my heels before an open fire in the trophy room, snarling, "Come hnyah, Isom, you black rascal," and generally qualifying myself as a Bourbon and a consumer of same.

Perhaps the most moonstruck campaign of whiskey advertising, and the one which easily deserves first place in the Around Robin Hood's Barn Sweepstakes, is that carried on for Cream of Kentucky Straight Bourbon. Of this series I saw nine examples, every one a collector's item. Each advertisement displayed a portrait of a person distinguished in some branch of the theater and beside it an analysis of his features indicating the facial characteristics typical of success. "Have you lips that spell SUCCESS?" barked the one starring Vincente Minnelli, the movie director, as it launched into a detailed examination of his lips. The inference was that since Mr. Minnelli had lips which spelled success (plump, unwrinkled, and full, with a deep, wide curve in the center of the upper one), you could be an extraordinary success as a host if you served guess what.

Had I paid no attention to this scientific revelation and gone along in my chosen field, which is mouth-breathing, everything would have been fine. But *I* had to go and compare the advertisements with each other and in doing so discover a striking fact: not only did I possess numerous physical attributes of success but *my face was actually a composite of the most important of them.* I had the "strong, big-boned jaw" of Glenn Anders; the "deep perpendicular furrow between the brows" of Michael Bartlett; the "distinct rows of horizontal undulating furrows immediately above the brows" of Harold Arlen; the "broad forehead, with prominent knotty bulges above the eyes" of Watson Barratt; the "eyebrows compact and regular, with hairs running smoothly in the same direction" of Sir Cedric Hardwicke; the "ears long and pale in color" of Paul Haakon; and the "mouth long, with a long upper lip and full, slightly drooping lower lip" of E. Y. Harburg. Though it was true my lips presented a "plump, unwrinkled" appearance, like Vincente Minnelli's, it was just as true "the lower lip presents a wrinkled appearance," like Russell Patterson's, especially after it has been slept in. In brief, I had everything calculated to bring hordes of theatrical managers and testimonial-seekers to my feet, yet here I was, a pitiful object tortured by irresolution and phantoms. Snatching at any straw which might make me a boy worthy of being chosen by the Four-H Clubs as a leader among his fellows, I disconnected the telephone and promptly drank off two bottles of the magic elixir at a high rate of speed. There are all sorts of apocryphal stories of how I was seen balancing myself on a coping four floors above the street; the truth is that I was simply seized with an attack of giddiness and went out for a breath of air. My goodness, you can't hang a man for *that!* What do you want me to do, shut myself up in a stuffy room and stare at the fine print under a lot of whiskey advertisements? . . . Answer me! For heaven's sake stop gaping at me with that inscrutable Mona Lisa expression of yours, will you?

Which Way to the Stylish Stouts?

THE NEXT TIME anybody around here tries to force a nine-day diet on me, this is my promissory note for a good swift kick in the pants. In fact, just the word "diet" may win some lucky boy or girl a free shiner. I don't want to reduce; I think I'm adorable just the way I am.

As one endowed with the muscles of a panther and morals to match, I have always treated my body like a fine precision instrument. At regular intervals—about five evenings a week—I immersed all the moving parts in a special alcohol preparation diluted with club soda; I religiously adhered to a

Spartan regimen of sweet potatoes, flour gravy and puddings of a high specific gravity. It was, therefore, something of a shock to discover recently that a little extra abdominal tissue had formed unbeknownst to me. I first detected it aboard a train to Hollywood, where I generally have my brain dry-cleaned for summer wear. Bending over to unlace my ghillies, I noticed a small bulge about the size of a junior rugby veiling the sternum, or breastbone. I pointed it out to the wife, or virago, and we shared a hearty chuckle. As the laughter was subsiding, the wretched creature deliberately harpooned me. "Better lay off those starches, lover," she advised. "I know a beanie when I see it." I did what any gentleman would do under the circumstances, and nursing my knuckles, spent the remainder of the trip in the lounge car, reconditioning myself with silver fizzes.

For a week after arriving at the studio, I concealed my tiny secret by wearing shirts a size too large. Gradually, however, I began to sense a cynical, almost callous attitude about me. Casual references to Falstaff and William Howard Taft cropped up in my friends' conversation. One morning, leafing through my secretary's notebook, I ran across a sketch of Man Mountain Dean bearing a crude resemblance to myself. To avoid any confusion, the dainty miss had captioned the lampoon "The Slave Driver." The slave driver examined his likeness pensively, and then, sponging the perspiration from his wee forehead, went out and bought the schedule of a nine-day diet.

The first day I nibbled the various fronds and chlorophyll indicated in the diet and felt normal, except for a slight fainting spell about four in the afternoon. Fortunately, as I was collapsing, I clutched at a passing ice-cream soda and regained my balance. Around eleven that evening, I suddenly burst into a fit of tears like an ingénue, flung myself on my bed, and began eating the bolster. On recovering my poise, I made a microscopic search of the icebox, which yielded nothing but a stalk of celery. I spent the night pacing the floor in vain. Twice I almost stumbled over what seemed to be a loaf of rye bread dotted with caraway seeds.

About midmorning the next day, while I conferred with my producer, he abruptly turned into a stack of flapjacks oozing maple sirup. "What's wrong with you?" he demanded nervously. "No writer ever looked at me like that before." I muttered some evasion and returned to my office to work. Try as I would, I could not get my mind off food; I kept dictating the most painstaking descriptions of the dishes my characters ate.

"Garry Bainbridge enters," I directed my secretary breathlessly. "He is a jolly, high-spirited youngster, big rather than fat. One look tells you he loves Boston cream pie, apple turnovers, and those delicious little chocolate éclairs. GARRY (*his voice as smooth as lemon icing*): 'Why, hello, Diomede, you look sweet enough to eat. Let's celebrate our betrothal at Fahnestock's Grill tonight. Personally I vote for cherrystone clams, pea soup, roast duckling, a wedge of cheesecake and four cups of coffee.' Diomede readily agrees and we dissolve to Fahnestock's Grill. . . . No, wait a minute, Miss Mink. Make that the kitchen of Fahnestock's Grill. I think the audience should see the food being prepared, don't you?"

I asked her to type up the scene and retired to the studio restaurant, where I dined off two sliced tomatoes and a cup of tea. Hedy Lamarr and Lana Turner sat at the next table in peekaboo blouses, but all I could see was the soufflé they were eating. I reeled back to the producer's office to get his reaction to my scene. He was phoning the casting department as I entered. "We don't need actors for this picture," I heard him snap. "Just some bicarbonate of soda." I tiptoed out, sped to the nearest barbecue, and ordered the largest steak ever served in Southern California. When I finished it, along toward nightfall, I engaged a room upstairs heavy with the odor of giblets, and sent for my typewriter. I still owe you seven days on that diet, girls. Try and catch me.

I Hardly Closed an Eye

WOULD ANYBODY like to know what I have always contended? . . . Thank you. I have always contended that a sensitive young man of good constitution, casting about for some uncrowded profession, could do worse than become a hypochondriac. The hours are your own, working conditions are perfection if you own an innerspring mattress, and the formidable mass of medical jargon employed by a hypochondriac entitles him to the respect accorded a physician once removed. Given a copy of Gray's *Anatomy,* a vapor kettle, and a bottle of benzoin, the variations are limitless.

I Hardly Closed an Eye

Though little more than a distinguished amateur in the field, I found good wincing recently in two somewhat divergent items: one a bulletin drawn from the *Proceedings of the Society for Experimental Biology and Medicine,* the other the August issue of *Superman,* the British health magazine. The title of the bulletin—"Pharmacology of Inflammation: III. Influences of Hygroscopic Agents on Irritation from Cigarette Smoke"—is no more portentous than its conclusions. I had not read beyond the title when I started ripping open my cigarettes in an agony of doubt. True, there was no trace of agents, beyond a suspicious bit of green felt which might have come from a Tyrolean hat of the sort they affect. But the bare possibility that *something* had crept in besides good old sun-dried burley was enough for baby, and I read the complicated experiment of the Messrs. Mulinos and Osborne with a mixture of fascinated horror and voluptuous yawns.

"We herewith report," state the authors, "a successful attempt to measure objectively the irritant properties of cigarette smoke. We used the conjunctival sac of rabbits according to the technic of Hirschhorn and Mulinos." Why the rabbit was made the butt of the research rather than, let us say, the mongoose or wapiti is not quite clear, but I assume Bunny must be the chain smoker of the animal kingdom. And, just in passing, it seems to me the investigators throw away that line about the sac a trifle too blandly. Conjunctival sacs do not grow on trees; I personally would be hard put to know where to pick one up. However, if the stories *I* hear are true, there are plenty of spots around the College of Physicians and Surgeons where you can get anything you want for a price.

Hardly ankle-deep in the bewildering chart on page 2, I soon confirmed what I half suspected—that I was a very sick boy indeed. The two hygroscopic agents usually employed in the manufacture of cigarettes, observed the bulletin carelessly, are glycerine and di-ethylene-glycol, "deemed necessary to maintain the proper moisture content of the cigarette." Rising leisurely and trampling down my family in passage, I repaired to the medicine chest and examined my features. There was no doubt about it—a thin film which could only be glycerine had formed over my eyeballs. I lit a cigarette with shaking hands and, as the cooling di-ethylene-glycol steadied the echoing ganglia, plunged back into the bulletin.

The actual mechanics of the test were absurdly simple to anyone possessing the slightest degree of intelligence and a master's degree in biochemistry. Unfortunately, I am still remembered in the academic halls as the boy who flunked four successive years of freshman trigonometry, and it is possible I missed a fine shade of meaning here and there. No matter how many times I read the phrase "In Fig. I, smoke from the burning cigarette which is protected from drafts by a jacket *h* . . . ammonia tube g . . . maintained by artificial means, by immersion of cylinder *f*, in a water bath," all I got was the smell of a wet sheepskin coat drying on a radiator and the soft tinkle of banjos in the quad. The upshot of the experiment, that cigarettes containing di-ethylene-glycol proved less irritating than those with glycerine, found me on a horizontal plane, softly humming "Brunonia, Mother of Men." It was not until I detected the footnote "This research was made possible by a grant from Philip Morris & Co., Ltd., Inc.," that everything suddenly came into sharp focus. So I had been present at the birth of an advertising campaign. Any day now I expect to see photographs of socially prominent rabbits lingering over their smokes in a rather smart hutch and murmuring, "It's di-ethylene-glycol two to one, you know. Just ask your conjunctival sac." In the meantime, if it's all right with Mulinos and Osborne, I'm on a cubeb wagon.

THE problems discussed in *Superman, the National Physical Culture Monthly*, if less general in nature, are certainly as acute. A correspondent identified as K.W.H. (Cheltenham) complains in the Question Box, "When I bend my head forward I hear a clicking noise and this is gradually getting more pronounced. What should I do to get rid of it?" Obviously, K.W.H. (Cheltenham) has accidentally swallowed some billiard balls and each time he bends his neck they kiss, yet instead of encouraging this young hypochondriac and urging him to develop his latent brilliance, the editors dismiss him with a snide little fanfaronade about his neck muscles. The same is true of a correspondent from Swindon, who writes, "I have a pain in the back which a doctor says is myosotis. I should like to know the treatment." To advise such an individual to restrict his consumption of fried food and pickles is an evasion. I do not presume to be Sir William Osler, but my guess is that our Swindon friend somehow ingested a sailmaker's needle (there are several retired sailmakers resident around Swindon). Or he may have had an experience similar to that of the noted vaudeville actor Bert Fitzgibbon. The latter arbitrated a dispute between two excited hoodlums and thereafter went about for a week complaining of a pain in the fleshy part of the leg, unaware he was harboring a .38-caliber slug.

Perhaps the most promising timber of all, however, is the suppliant signing himself "W.H.S. (Brownhills)." "Please criticize my measurements and feats. Am I large or small-boned?" he implores, appending a series of details concerning his chest, waist, and biceps. I believe I know what is troubling W.H.S. He spent the previous evening at a shebeen vying with some friends to see who could pick up the heaviest toddy, and has awakened with thc strange sensation that his shape has altered. By merely crooking his finger, he manages to knock over a lamp in a far corner, but when he prepares to rise, his feet hardly touch the floor. It is hardly scientific, therefore, to suggest, as does the editor, "You should get busy with progressive heavy exercise." Even the very lightest exercise, like combing the hair, might result in complete collapse. The only medication worth the name is to swarm back into bed with a mild restorative, like a quart of Irish, and lie there worrying. . . . *Say,* could that be a solution for all of us?

Send No Money Honey

I HAVE A WELL-DEFINED SUSPICION, bounded on the south by Fortieth Street and the north by Fifty-seventh, that anybody venturing into the Times Square area who was not already sick of phosphorescent carnations is, by now, sick of phosphorescent carnations. Exactly when the craze for these luminous hybrids captured the popular imagination is uncertain—possibly during the dimout. At any rate, since then every midtown cranny too small for a watchmaker, a popcorn machine, or a publisher's remainders boasts its own little altar of black velvet from which carnations and brooches of debatable value give off a spectral greenish glow. It is not altogether clear, incidentally, whether people buy them to wear or to worship in private. The only time I believe I ever saw one off the leash was at the Rialto Theater, when a woman's head, radiating a distinct nimbus, rose in a grisly, disembodied fashion and floated past me up the aisle. I assume it was illuminated from below by a phosphorescent corsage, but it may merely have been an ordinary disembodied head viewing the feature at a reduced rate of admission.

The vogue could be discounted as a sheerly local phenomenon except that a short time ago a prominent jobber of glowing novelties decided to invade the mail-order field. Hiring the back cover of a breezy magazine called *Laff*, the Glow-in-the-Dark Necktie Company of Chicago exhibited a twinkling four-in-hand flashing the words "WILL YOU KISS ME IN THE DARK, BABY?" accompanied by this text:

Girls Can't Resist this KISS ME NECKTIE as it GLOWS in the Dark! By Day a Lovely Swank Tie . . . By Night a Call to Love in Glowing Words! . . . Here's the most amazing spectacular necktie that you ever wore, a smart, wrinkleproof, tailored cravat, which at night is a thrilling sensation! It's smart, superb class by day, and just imagine in the dark it seems like a necktie of compelling allure, sheer magic! Like a miracle of light there comes a pulsing, glowing question—WILL YOU KISS ME IN THE DARK, BABY? Think of the surprise, the awe you will cause! There's no trick, no hidden batteries, no switches or foolish horseplay, but a thing of beauty as the question emerges gradually to life, touched by the wand of darkness, and your girl will gasp with wonder as it takes form so amazingly. . . . Send no money, here's all you do . . .

However unpredictable its reception by the beau monde, there is no gainsaying the romantic appeal of the glowing necktie in terms of theater. Before some energetic dramatist weaves the idea into a smash operetta or Leon Leonidoff preempts it for one of his opulent Music Hall presentations, I hasten to stake out my claim with the following playlet. If Metro-Goldwyn-Mayer would like it as a vehicle for Greer Garson (and I'm ready to throw in a whiffle-tree and two wheels), I shall be wearing a corned-beef sandwich this evening in the third booth at the Brass Rail. Just walk by rapidly and drop the three dollars on the floor.

[*Scene: The conservatory of the country club at Heublein's Fens, Ohio. Fern Replevin, an utterly lovely creature of twenty-four whose mouth wanders at will over her features in the manner of Greer Garson's, sits lost in dreams, watching a cirrus formation in the moonlit sky. Offstage the usual Saturday-night dance is in progress, and as mingled laughter and music drift in to Fern, she softly hums the air the orchestra is playing, "If Love Should Call."*]

FERN:

If love should call, and you were I,
And I were you, and love should call,

How happy I could be with I,
And you with you, if love should call.
Your shoulders broad, your instep arched,
Without your kiss my lips are parched.
For love comes late, and now, and soon,
At midnight's crack and blazing noon.
My arms are ready, the wine is heady,
If love should call.

(*Lafcadio Replevin, Fern's father, enters. He belongs to the Vigorous and Tweedy school—is headmaster, in fact—is leader in his community and a man who knows his way around the block, if no further. He has, as the saying goes, a groatsworth of wit in a guinea-sized noddle. Maybe the saying doesn't go just this way, but it certainly describes Lafcadio.*)

LAFCADIO: Oh, there you are, daughter; I've been looking all over for you. Why aren't you inside dancing with your fiancé, Fleetwood Rumsey, that is by far the richest man in town and owner of feed mills galore throughout the vicinity? There hasn't been any tiffin' between you, has there?

FERN (*indicating some scones and tea on the table*): Only what you see on this tray.

LAFCADIO: Then why are you staring at those clouds so pensively?

FERN: Perhaps I'm more cirrus-minded than the other girls.

LAFCADIO: Well, I don't like to see you moon around. As for me, I'm going in and have a drink with that new librarian. She's as thin as a *lath* and pretty *stucco* on herself, but I guess we can get *plastered.* (*He exits chuckling. Sunk in reverie, Fern is unaware that a man has emerged from behind a rubber plant and is regarding her narrowly. Rex Beeswanger is thirty-odd, a thoroughbred from his saturnine eyebrow to the tip of his well-polished shoe. His clothes, which he wears with casual elegance, bear an unmistakable metropolitan stamp. He is shod by Thom McAn, gloved by Fownes, belted by Hickok, and cravatted by Glow-in-Dark.*)

REX (*softly*): If you don't love him, why go through with it?

FERN (*whirling*): Oh! You startled me.

REX: Did I?

FERN: Did you what?

REX: Startle you.

FERN: Yes. I mean I was sunk in a reverie, and you spoke to me suddenly, and that startled me.

REX: You see things clearly, don't you? You're a very direct person.

FERN: Am I?

REX: Are you what?

FERN: A very direct person.

REX: Yes. When I startled you out of the reverie in which you were sunk, you didn't pretend I hadn't. That would have been cheap. And you're not cheap.

FERN: What are we talking about?

REX: Does it matter? Does anything matter but silver slanting rain on the cruel lilacs and compassion in the heart's deep core?

FERN: Who are you? You haven't even told me your name.

REX: Just a bird of passage. Call me Rex Beeswanger if you like.

FERN (*savoring it*): Rex Beeswanger. I've always wanted to know someone named Rex Beeswanger. It's—it's instinct with springtime and the song of larks.

REX: May I kiss you?

FERN: Oh, Rex, you've got to give me time to think. We've known each other less than forty-eight hours.

REX (*fiercely*): Is that all love means to you—narrow little conventions, smug barriers holding two kinsprits apart? I thought you finer than that.

FERN: Yes, but there's so much light in here. It's like a cafeteria or something. (*For answer, Rex extinguishes the lamp. Instantly the legend "WILL YOU KISS ME IN THE DARK, BABY?" springs into relief on his tie. The music inside swells and, silhouetted against the window, Fern lifts her voice in vibrant melody.*)

FERN:

You glowed in the dark, I saw your spark,
You left your mark on me.
You're wrinkleproof, and so aloof,

You made a goof of me.
I might have been coy with another boy,
But not when you said "Ahoy" to me.
I'm a pearl of a girl, so give me a whirl.
Ah, don't be a perfect churl to me.

(*As Fern and Rex lock lips, harsh light floods the room, and Fleetwood Rumsey, his bull neck distended with rage, stands glaring balefully at the pair.*)

FLEETWOOD: So this is what gives out behind my back.

FERN (*returning his ring*): Fleetwood, I think there is something you ought to know.

FLEETWOOD: In due time. First, I mean to show this meddling upstart how we deal with kiss thieves in Heublein's Fens. (*Sidestepping nimbly, Rex pins him in a grip of steel and slowly forces him to his knees.*)

REX: *Les jeux sont faits,* "Short Weight" Rumsey!

FLEETWOOD (*paling*): You—you know me then?

REX: Your leering visage adorns every rogue's gallery in the country. (*Encircling his captive's wrists with a set of shiny handcuffs*) Thanks to you, Miss Replevin, a notorious malefactor has received his just lumps. He had been adulterating his poultry mash with sawdust and subspecification brans, causing a serious crimp in egg production.

FERN: My woman's intuition warned me. I wouldn't wipe my feet on the best part of him.

REX: Governmental appreciation will follow in due cou We have every reason to believe him the agent of a foreig power.

FLEETWOOD (*gutturally*): I get efen wiz you for zis zome time, Mr. Rex Beeswanger!

REX: Take him away, boys. (*Fleetwood is removed by two burly operatives as a corps de ballet of forty trained dancers swirls about Fern and Rex, symbolizing the gratitude of local poultrymen and 4-H Clubs alike. As the spectacle reaches a climax, the ushers, equipped with phosphorescent truncheons, flit through the darkened theater like myriad fireflies and awaken the audience. On second thought, I don't believe I'll be in the Brass Rail tonight after all. There's no sense sticking my chin out.*)

CURTAIN